Effective of Teaching Numeracy

For The National Mathematics Framework

Effective Teaching of Numeracy

For The National Mathematics Framework

Valsa Koshy

Hodder & Stoughton

A MEMBER OF THE HODDER HEADLINE GROUP

Orders: please contact Bookpoint Ltd, 78 Milton Park, Abingdon, Oxon OX14 4TD. Telephone: (44) 01235 827720, Fax: (44) 01235 400454. Lines are open from 9.00–6.00, Monday to Saturday, with a 24 hour message answering service. Email address: orders@bookpoint.co.uk

British Library Cataloguing in Publication Data
A catalogue record for this title is available from The British Library

ISBN 0 340 753900

First published 1999
Impression number   10 9 8 7 6 5 4 3 2 1
Year   2005 2004 2003 2002 2001 2000 1999

Copyright © 1999 Valsa Koshy

Typeset by Wearset, Boldon, Tyne and Wear.
Printed in Great Britain for Hodder & Stoughton Educational, a division of Hodder Headline Plc, 338 Euston Road, London NW1 3BH by J. W. Arrowsmith, Bristol.

Contents

Acknowledgements

My aim in writing this book is to support teachers to develop numeracy skills in children. I have drawn on two main sources for selecting the content of the book: my experience as an in-service provider for over 17 years and my personal research into aspects of mathematics education. Although it is impossible to name all the people who have influenced my thinking over the past few years, I would like to express my gratitude to all of them. I would especially like to thank the following people:

◆ Professor Margaret Brown, at Kings College, London, whose work on children's understanding of place value and decimals, in 1981, provided the first spark to my interest in children's strategies in working with aspects of number. Her viewpoints and research have inspired me ever since.

◆ All the teachers I have worked with and from whom I have learnt a great deal. They have kept me aware of an important principle in providing in-service support: *the need to provide practical and manageable suggestions within a framework which facilitates thinking and reflection.*

◆ My husband Ron Casey, who convinced me of the importance of teachers' own subject knowledge and high expectations in raising children's achievement. I thank him also for encouraging me to write this book.

I dedicate this book to my daughter Elizabeth. Watching her development of numerical skills for 24 years — from early counting on fingers to the present — has contributed to my own learning process.

Introduction

The teaching of numeracy has been a matter of concern for the last few years. Reports from the Office of Standards in Education (Ofsted) and results of international comparisons have highlighted that all is not well with many aspects of teaching numeracy. Therefore, it is no surprise to find the effective teaching of numeracy on the national agenda. After many months of preparation, a **National Numeracy Strategy** is being implemented from September 1999. The National Numeracy Task Force, set up by the government, has produced a set of recommendations for improving children's numerical competence. Schools have been provided with a **Framework for teaching mathematics** which sets out teaching programmes and guidance on how to plan, teach and assess numeracy.

A careful study of the *Framework* reveals that the classroom teacher needs to address two aspects in order to implement the National Numeracy Strategy: a sound knowledge of the content and an effective teaching style. This poses a big, but exciting challenge. At the present time there are many questions buzzing in teachers' heads: is the pendulum of change swinging again, from individual discovery learning to group work and now to whole-class teaching? How do we know what is the right way to teach? What should we do with calculators? How do we change teaching styles? How is 'good practice' defined? How do I implement mental mathematics without reverting back to the timed-tests which caused fear and frustration in many youngsters in the past?

The purpose of this book is to offer support to teachers as they consider some of these questions and to begin to look at this new initiative which has many positive features. By considering research, theory and the practical implications of teaching numeracy to children, readers are invited to join me in an interactive exploration of aspects of numeracy. They are provided with practical suggestions and opportunities for reflection on the way, so that they will be able to make 'informed' decisions with greater understanding and confidence.

The book is divided into six chapters. **Chapter 1** sets out the context of the book and provides a brief account of the background to the National Numeracy Strategy. Recent research and developments in the teaching of numeracy and the recommendations for improving teaching strategies are considered. This chapter also considers the definition of numeracy adopted by the National Numeracy Strategy and its implications.

Effective teaching of numeracy does not happen by accident; it evolves from the concerted efforts of people who are involved with implementation at each level of school organisation contributing their understanding of the different aspects of teaching numeracy. In order to enhance that understanding, this chapter lists a number of factors which influence the effectiveness of teaching numeracy. These are taken from previously published, official documents and the *Framework for teaching mathematics*. The significance of the recommendations for 'good practice' is discussed with illustrative examples.

Chapter 2 deals with aspects of teaching 'number'. In order to build a sound framework of knowledge about 'number' children need to learn facts, practise skills, make connections between concepts and be able to apply their knowledge. The three strands of the *Framework* which are directly related to learning about number – Numbers and the Number System, Calculations, and Solving Problems – are analysed and discussed. The importance of place value, including decimals is emphasised throughout. This chapter also includes practical guidance on methods of calculation and how teachers can encourage children to be effective problem solvers.

The whole of **Chapter 3** is devoted to mental and oral mathematics. These aspects of numeracy have been given prominence in the National Numeracy Strategy; they are also part of the daily mathematics lesson. My personal research shows that teaching mental mathematics is an area which many teachers feel anxious about. So, this chapter lists and explains teaching strategies which practising teachers can draw on in their efforts to encourage their children to be proficient in mental mathematics. A range of exemplar activities are included along with practical suggestions for grouping, classroom organisation and differentiation for teaching mental mathematics.

Chapter 4 focuses on issues relating to planning, teaching and assessing numeracy. By drawing on the recommendations in the *Framework for teaching mathematics*, long-term, medium-term and short-term planning are discussed. Discussion is also focused on good planning habits and how to evaluate plans. Emphasis is placed on aspects of planning the daily mathematics lesson. Examples of daily plans, designed by practising teachers, are provided for the reader to consider their effectiveness. Different models of activities which can be used in the daily lesson are presented with supporting commentary. A significant part of this chapter is devoted to aspects of assessing children's learning. Effective ways of gathering information about what children can do and understand are discussed. A **Formative Assessment** recording system is introduced. The value of analysing children's mistakes is emphasised through a practical exercise.

Chapter 5 focuses on the role of Information and Communications Technology (ICT) in the teaching of numeracy. We live in a technological world. Computers and calculators are easily available and there is no doubt that they are powerful resources in teaching mathematics. There is much confusion and an emergence of mixed messages about the use of calculators in the primary school. These are discussed and sensible ways of using calculators for improving numeracy skills are presented. I have also provided some practical examples of using computer programmes – both content free and structured – to enhance children's numerical competence and problem-solving skills.

Chapter 6, the final chapter of this book, deals with a challenging topic – how to achieve differentiation in the daily mathematics lesson. This complex issue is analysed and some practical ways to meet the needs of children across the ability spectrum are suggested. A list of publications and resources is given for reference.

I have attempted to write this book in an interactive style and the reader is invited to be engaged in some tasks whilst reading the book. Although these are optional, I have included them because I believe that theories and principles need personalising to be effective. We are embarking on one of the most challenging and exciting journeys in mathematics education. I hope this book will provide you with a clear set of directions for you to enjoy that journey.

Chapter 1

Setting the context

Background

Raising standards in mathematics achievement through effective teaching of numeracy is now a national priority. However, our awareness of the problems experienced by children in their understanding and application of numerical skills is not new. Concerns about school leavers' numeracy skills were voiced by James Callahan (1976) who expressed his discomfort arising from complaints from industry that new recruits did not have the basic tools necessary to do their jobs. HMI reports (1978; 1979) raised concerns about pupils not being able to apply their numerical skills in a variety of situations. Surveys by the Assessment of Performance Unit (1982; 1985) and research evidence provided by the Concepts in Secondary Mathematics and Science project (Brown, 1981) highlighted difficulties experienced by children in their understanding of aspects of number, both in primary and secondary schools.

So, the need for developing children's numeracy skills is not a new idea; it has been emphasised in official reports for many decades. People's perceptions of what 'being numerate' entails have changed, over the years, from being able to 'carry out number operations' to possessing a 'sound understanding of the number system and how to apply this knowledge in all contexts'. This positive shift in the meaning of numeracy is reflected in the following statements in 'Mathematics Counts' (The Cockcroft Report, 1982):

> We would wish the word 'numerate' to imply the possession of two attributes. The first of these is an 'at-homeness' with numbers and an ability to make use of mathematical skills which enables an individual to cope with the practical mathematical demands of everyday life. The second is an ability to have some appreciation and understanding of information which is presented in mathematical terms, for instance in graphs, charts or tables or by reference to percentage increase or decrease. Taken together, these imply that a numerate person should be expected to be able to appreciate and understand some of the ways in which mathematics can be used as a means of communication. (para 39)

However, ten years on, Ofsted (1993) pointed out that the 'feel for number' and the 'at homeness' with number highlighted in the Cockcroft Report were frequently neglected. A review carried out in schools by Ofsted (1994) confirmed the above concern:

> . . . pupils learn 'tricks' and 'games' which yield the right answer in exercises. The repetitious nature of exercises generates boredom and too little time is spent remedying weaknesses. For some, the crucial skills such as understanding place-value do not get embedded early enough. For others, pencil and paper algorithms are introduced too early. Mental arithmetic and the development of patterns in number which aid calculation have been neglected for a number of years. (p. 21)

During the interim years, between 1982 and 1993, a statutory National Curriculum in mathematics was introduced (DES, 1989) which addressed the need for a major focus on teaching number.

What is numeracy?

The sentiments expressed in the previous section are stressed in the definition given to 'numeracy' by the National Numeracy Task Force (DfEE, 1998) and is adopted for the *Framework for teaching mathematics* (DfEE, 1999), hitherto referred to as the *Framework*:

> Numeracy at Key Stages 1 and 2 is a proficiency which involves a confidence and competence with numbers and measures. It requires an understanding of the number system, a repertoire of computational skills and an inclination and ability to solve number problems in a variety of contexts. Numeracy also demands practical understanding of the ways in which information is gathered by counting and measuring, and is presented in graphs, diagrams, charts and tables. (p. 4)

One of the main objectives of introducing a National Numeracy Strategy is to enable children to work both confidently and with greater independence. Teachers have a major role to play in making this happen.

So where do we start? A good place is to take a close look at the list of objectives for teaching numeracy as presented in the *Framework* (DfEE, 1999). The list is designed to support children to:

◆ have a sense of the size of a number and where it fits into the number system;

◆ know by heart number facts such as number bonds, multiplication tables, doubles and halves;

◆ use what they know by heart to figure out answers mentally;

◆ calculate accurately and efficiently, both mentally and with pencil and paper, drawing on a range of calculation strategies;

◆ recognise when it is appropriate to use a calculator, and be able to do so effectively;

◆ make sense of number problems, including non-routine problems, and recognise the operations needed to solve them;

◆ explain their methods and reasoning using correct mathematical terms;

◆ judge whether their answers are reasonable and have strategies for checking them where necessary;

◆ suggest suitable units of measuring, and make sensible estimates of measurements; and

◆ explain and make predictions from the numbers in graphs, diagrams, charts and tables. (p. 4)

This broad and sensible interpretation of the term numeracy makes the National Numeracy Strategy an exciting and useful initiative. It can be seen that, in terms of content, the above list includes most aspects of mathematics. It reassures us that the emphasis is on adopting more effective teaching methods and focusing on important aspects of numeracy which have been neglected in the past. One example of this is the need for more systematic teaching of mental mathematics.

Aims of the National Numeracy Strategy

As well as providing a definition of numeracy, the two declared aims in the Final Report of the Numeracy Task Force (DfEE, 1998) should also offer reassurance to those who are involved in teaching mathematics at all levels. The first aim – raising achievement – is timely within the context of the current concern about national standards of British children's numerical competence, as highlighted in studies such as the Third International Mathematics and Science Study (TIMMS, 1997). In view of this concern the government has set targets for raising children's achievement in mathematics; support for the achievement of this aim is provided through the implementation of the National Numeracy Strategy.

The second aim is to promote 'good quality' teaching of mathematics in our schools. This, again, should reassure those who feel anxious about a possible return to 'drill and practice, learning of rules without understanding and children being encouraged in meaningless regurgitation of facts'. The list I have given above has turned generations of pupils 'off' mathematics and has left many adults with fear and anxiety about the subject. The twin aims of the Numeracy Strategy should herald a new dawn for mathematics teaching and learning in Britain.

As I have mentioned in the introduction, the purpose of this book is to offer support to all those who are involved in implementing the National Numeracy Strategy. It is designed to provide the reader with practical suggestions as well as opportunities for reflection.

Recent recommendations for the effective teaching of numeracy

What practical recommendations and guidance are available to teachers in their pursuit of excellence? A good place to start is to consider recent research and developments in mathematics education and take note of recommendations for the effective teaching of numeracy.

Mathematics Enhancement Programme

The following recommendations were put forward by the Mathematics Enhancement Project, set up by Professor David Burghes (Burghes, 1999) and designed to improve and enhance mathematics teaching and learning in the UK. Its recommendations, the author points out, are based on an international comparative project (Kassel Project, 1996) which led to subsequent observations of teaching in countries like Hungary, Poland, Singapore and Japan. The 'main thrust' of the project, as he describes it, is on *'putting the teacher back as the focus of learning'* with:

◆ encouragement for whole-class teaching, with less individualised work;

◆ stress on writing and speaking mathematics precisely and correctly;

◆ emphasis on numeracy (including mental work) and application;

◆ homework used as an integral part of the learning process rather than as 'add on' extras. (p. 26)

Two aspects are emphasised by Burghes (1999) in offering advice to teachers: first, the adoption of a whole-class, active and interactive teaching style, and second the need to consider 'mathematics as an exact science, with proper notation, equations balancing and each logical statement properly explained; no sloppiness, no short hand notation – it has to be mathematically correct'. (p. 27)

Burghes and Merttens (1997) put forward a 'Blueprint for Numeracy' which the authors maintain can be implemented 'relatively easily' and at little cost, to enhance our nation's numeracy skills. They recommend that whatever is done should start in the early years of schooling. As their checklist of 10 key points to improve numeracy has been found useful by practising teachers, the full list is given below:

1 There should be more *whole-class*, interactive teaching with the class at times organised so that every child is focused on the teacher.

2 Lessons should begin with 'quick-fire' mental work and there should be a short daily slot of oral work for all children.

3 Key facts such as number bonds and tables, and key skills such as rounding up/down, adding multiples of 10 and doubling, should be learnt and practised regularly, both orally and in written from, until there is instant recall.

4 An accurate 'number line' should be displayed prominently in the class room, positioned so that it is accessible for children to see and touch.

5 Pupils should have their own 'number cards' (units, tens and hundreds to start with, increasing to thousands and decimals as the children get older). These can be laid out in front of them as an aid, and to show response to, mental work.

6 Children should be encouraged to lay out their written mathematics in neat and orderly manner and a spoken vocabulary, using correct and precise terminology, should be explicitly developed. As an example to pupils, all teachers' work, written and spoken, must be mathematically correct and precise.

7 Investigations must be meaningful, logical and should lead to a definite goal.

8 Calculators should not be used until the later years of Primary school. At this stage children should be taught to use them correctly and effectively and not as a substitute for mental calculation.

9 Mathematics should be taught as a separate subject in Primary schools, although opportunities to link with other subjects should be exploited to the full.

10 Mathematics lessons should be daily and timetabled as early in the day as possible.

All the above recommendations, which the authors describe as being based on 'common sense' are in fact incorporated into the National Numeracy Strategy.

Effective teachers of numeracy

In a research project involving 90 teachers and over 2000 pupils, the research team at Kings College (Askew *et al*, 1997b) explored the knowledge, beliefs and practices of a sample of teachers who were effective in teaching numeracy. In this project effectiveness was defined on the basis of children's average gain in numeracy scores over a year compared to other classes in the same year group.

Some of the listed distinguishing features of 'highly effective' teachers are given below. Effective teachers of numeracy believe that:

◆ being numerate requires having a network of connections between different mathematical ideas;

◆ pupils develop strategies and networks of ideas by being challenged to think, through explaining, listening and problem-solving;

◆ teachers should intervene when necessary to assist the pupil to become more efficient in the use of calculating strategies.

The research team identified three models of beliefs held by teachers about the teaching of numeracy. These orientations or models offer practising teachers opportunities to reflect on their own beliefs and styles of teaching. The authors acknowledge that the three groups of teachers represent 'ideal types' in that no teacher is 'likely to fit exactly within the framework of beliefs' and many will combine characteristics of two or more styles. The three orientations put forward by the team are:

◆ **connectionist** – beliefs based around both valuing pupil's methods and teaching effective strategies with an emphasis on establishing connections within mathematics;

◆ **transmission** – beliefs based around the primacy of teaching and a view of mathematics as a collection of separate routines and procedures; and

◆ **discovery** – beliefs based around the primacy of learning and a view of mathematics as being discovered by pupils.

In terms of classroom teaching the connectionists showed children the 'interconnections between concepts' such as fractions, decimals and percentages and invited children to offer explanations, whilst the transmission teachers taught their children methods which obtained 'quicker' results. The discovery teacher placed much emphasis on individual children setting their own pace, and viewed mathematics as 'mostly separate elements'. The 'connectionists' were the most effective in teaching numeracy.

Factors influencing the effective teaching of numeracy

Although it is difficult to provide a definition of 'good practice' in teaching and learning mathematics, research findings and the views of mathematics educationists who have spent many years reflecting on issues, as well as the collective wisdom expressed in HMI reports, together provide some insights into what contributes to effective teaching and learning of mathematics. The *Framework for teaching mathematics* also provides guidance on factors that influence effective teaching of numeracy. Drawing on these sources, I will now attempt to present a list of critical factors which I believe will have an impact on the teaching of numeracy.

1 Planning

Good planning is of major importance. Well planned lessons will show clear objectives, progression of ideas and evidence of assessment of whether the objectives of the lesson have been met. Teachers should plan learning tasks with high expectations of their children and teach them to as many pupils as possible, differentiating as and when necessary. The *Framework* offers detailed guidelines on planning for long-term, medium-term and short-term. However, it is the teachers' understanding of their children's learning needs, aptitudes and learning styles which ultimately makes a teaching plan effective.

2 Teaching styles

The National Numeracy Task Force (DfEE, 1998, p. 18) recommends 'whole-class teaching' for a considerable amount of time as a means of raising achievement and making numeracy lessons more effective. As Figure 1.1 shows, the structure of the daily lesson has built into it a high proportion of whole class teaching and a 'direct' and 'interactive' teaching style is recommended.

What do we mean by direct teaching? A clear description of direct teaching is provided in the *Framework*:

> High quality direct teaching is oral, interactive and lively. It is not achieved by adopting a simplistic formula of 'drill and practice' and lecturing the class, or by expecting pupils to teach themselves from books. It is a two-way process in which pupils are expected to play an active part by answering questions, contributing points to discussions, and explaining and demonstrating their method to the class. (p. 11)

The features of good direct teaching listed in the *Framework* take into account many of the recommendations for 'good' quality teaching from past

Clear Start to Lesson		
Whole–class	◆ mental and oral work to rehearse and sharpen skills	**About 5 to 10 minutes**

Main Teaching and Pupil Activities		
Whole–class/Groups/ Pairs/Individuals	◆ clear objectives shared with pupils ◆ interactive/direct teaching input ◆ pupils clear about what to do next ◆ practical and/or written work on the same theme for all the class ◆ if group work, usually differentiated at no more than 3 levels of difficulty, with focused teaching of 1 or 2 groups for part of the time ◆ continued interaction and intervention ◆ misconceptions identified	**About 30 to 40 minutes**

Plenary		
Whole–class	◆ feedback from children to identify progress and sort misconceptions ◆ summary of key ideas, what to remember ◆ links made to other work, next steps discussed ◆ work set to do at home	**About 10 to 15 minutes**

Figure 1.1 **A typical daily lesson recommended in the National Numeracy Strategy**

literature. These are presented below, with some explanations. It may be worthwhile for you to reflect on these elements and consider which of them are already part of your teaching and which need to be attended to.

The elements which constitute effective 'direct teaching' are:

◆ **Directing**

Children are told, at the beginning of the lesson both the objectives of the lesson and the order of events. This should help them to feel more responsible for achieving the objectives. They are told what to do and what to remember whilst carrying out the tasks; this may include advice on how to record or the methodology for constructing and labelling graphs.

◆ **Instructing**

This would involve giving sequenced instruction on how to carry out a written algorithm for subtraction or explaining how to estimate a correct solution. Giving instructions to the whole class on how to read and interpret a railway time-table or a pie chart saves time for the teacher who may have, in the past, explained procedures to small groups.

◆ **Demonstrating**

Showing children how a number line can be used to judge the 'nearness' of a number to a specified number or for rounding numbers is an example of demonstration. Demonstrations are needed for both mastering a skill such as using a ruler or for developing conceptual understanding of how the place value system is based on the principle of grouping. Again, in the past, many teachers may have tended to do these in small groups. Whole class demonstrations on mathematical aspects are likely to invite more variety and a richer quality of responses from the children.

◆ **Explaining and illustrating**

This would involve giving clear and correct explanations of mathematical words and symbols as well as exploring rules. Explaining that the principle of 'carrying' in addition is related to place value conventions would be an example of this.

◆ **Questioning and discussing**

The quality of children's learning depends of the quality of questions you ask. During class discussions children should be asked to share their mathematical thinking and explain their methods. Within whole-class discussions, children can be split into pairs and small groups before coming together to give feedback to the whole class. Discussion of problem-solving strategies and giving reasons for making decisions

are particularly valuable in developing children's confidence in
tackling unfamiliar and complex work.

◆ **Consolidating**
Children need to be challenged about their ideas and methods; they
also need to have opportunities for reinforcement and for refining
ideas. During plenary sessions, for example, children can be asked to
list one or two new ideas they have learnt, or one idea they would like
to explore in more depth. Consolidation can also take the form of a
'directed' task for homework.

◆ **Evaluating children's responses**
The high level of oral work recommended by the Numeracy Strategy
will provide the teacher with many opportunities for probing reasons
for pupils' responses and for making assessments of their learning.
During evaluations, children can be reassured that making mistakes
and being stuck are worthwhile experiences for making progress.

◆ **Summarising**
During the plenary or at the end of a task it is good to encourage
children to make presentations, bringing various elements of
mathematical learning together. Poster presentations have been found
particularly useful by teachers who have told the children, in advance,
that they will making a presentation on a particular aspect of
mathematics to the rest of the class.

3 The role of assessment

Effective teacher assessment is central to successful planning and teaching of
mathematics. As the numeracy strategy is implemented, new and more
efficient ways of assessing children should also be explored. Within a well
paced lesson, the teacher needs to develop a faster, more dynamic and
flexible way of gathering information about the children. Identifying and
addressing children's mistakes and misconceptions will need to become a
part of the daily lesson. Chapter 4 deals with formative assessment in greater
detail.

4 Mental mathematics

The importance of children developing mental strategies is emphasised in the
Numeracy Strategy. Mental and Oral mathematics is to be a regular feature in
the daily lesson. It is important to offer a variety of tasks to children – some
involving instant recall of number facts, some designed to develop an
understanding of concepts and others specifically designed to teach mental
strategies for calculations. Chapter 3 focuses on mental mathematics.

5 Attitudes

Finally, we all know that we learn better if we enjoy what we are learning. Teachers who are on our Numeracy courses have told us that children do enjoy the pace and the structure of the daily mathematics lessons and that they are responding positively to teachers' higher expectations. Children appreciate being told what they are doing and why. The National Numeracy Strategy has provided a climate for teachers to set high expectations and challenges for their children, which, in turn, should motivate them not only to learn more effectively, but to develop positive attitudes to learning mathematics.

Summary

In this chapter I have attempted to describe the context of the National Numeracy Strategy. Concerns expressed about the deficiencies of children's numerical skills, over the past few years, are reported. A definition of 'numeracy' and what it entails provides a focus which, it is hoped, will be illuminated by the various strands of the text in subsequent chapters. Recent research and recommendations for the effective teaching of numeracy have also been described.

Chapter 2

Aspects of teaching number

In the previous chapter we considered the definition of numeracy. Numeracy was described as a proficiency which involves confidence and competence with numbers. A careful study of the *Framework for teaching mathematics* highlights the importance placed by the Numeracy Strategy on children dealing with all aspects of number which, in turn, will enable them to tackle mathematical problems with confidence. This chapter is, therefore, devoted to a consideration of how we can help children to develop a *feel* for number.

Children's numerical competence or their *feel* for number emanates from knowing their number facts, practising skills, developing a conceptual understanding of number, relationships between number operations and between numbers. Development of problem-solving skills and fostering a positive attitude to mathematics are also important. Key issues relating to all these aspects of number are dealt with in this chapter.

A framework for teaching and learning about number

The five specific objectives of learning mathematics put forward by HMI (1985) provide us with a very helpful framework when considering what the effective teaching of numeracy entails. These five objectives are:

◆ Facts

◆ Skills

◆ Conceptual structures

◆ General strategies

◆ Personal qualities

How these objectives can be incorporated into your numeracy teaching is now discussed.

Facts

Children need to learn and remember correct facts. They need to learn mathematical terms such as number names, names of shapes and names of operations. They need to recognise and use mathematical signs such as +, −,

×, ÷, = and so on. Mathematical notation, such as decimal points and percentages (%), needs to be recognised and the meanings understood. Remembering facts such as $5 + 5 = 10$ or $6 \times 7 = 42$ is useful for two reasons: first, such facts when committed to memory make it possible for children to use them fluently and with speed and secondly, from 'known facts', it is possible to derive new facts; for example, if you know $5 + 5 = 10$, then $5 + 6$ can be worked out with reasonable ease. Learning facts, therefore, empowers children.

The use of correct mathematical vocabulary is stressed in the *Framework*. All schools are provided with a mathematical vocabulary book (DfEE, 1999) and all model lesson plans which are distributed for training purposes focus on key mathematical terms. Displays of vocabulary on the walls will enable children to be constantly reminded of mathematical words. Children's own glossary of mathematical words, or mathematical fact books, will help them to internalise the mathematical terms more effectively. Examples of children's mathematical glossaries can be seen elsewhere in this book. As children learn more mathematical ideas, facts and conventions, their conceptual framework becomes expanded. The structure of the *daily mathematics lessons* provides many opportunities for children to learn and rehearse facts.

Skills

The Cockcroft Report (1982) describes skills as an integral part of learning mathematics and explains that:

> Skills include not only the use of number facts and the standard computational procedures of arithmetic and algebra, but also of any well established procedures which it is possible to carry out by the use of a routine. They need not only to be understood and embedded in the conceptual structure but also to be brought up to the level of immediate recall or fluency of performance by regular practice. (para 240)

Skills include number operations and routine procedures. These are useful and should be taught and practised. However, the over use of time on the practice of skills has been the subject of much criticism in both HMI and Ofsted reports. In many classrooms the practising of skills is often based on exercises taken from commercially produced text books. The emphasis on oral communication of methods and procedures and the recommendations for well-paced daily mathematics lessons in the Numeracy Strategy may replace the over-reliance on text books by the teacher providing demonstrated examples followed by only the necessary amount of practice of skills.

Children often practice skills without understanding the rationale behind learnt procedures. As a result they make mistakes which arise out of forgotten or misapplied rules. The Numeracy Strategy urges teachers to study children's mistakes and misconceptions and be proactive in addressing them. As children's mistakes provide teachers with very useful insights into their understanding of number, mistakes are dealt with, in more detail, in Chapter 4.

Conceptual structures

The Cockcroft Report (1982) describes conceptual structures as 'richly interconnecting bodies of knowledge'. Whilst skills may be learnt through demonstrations only, concepts are ideas which need to be integrated into an existing framework of knowledge. Within this framework concepts are inter-related. HMI (1985) puts forward a powerful argument in favour of aiming for a sound conceptual understanding; this is quoted below because of its significance for the implementation of the Numeracy Strategy. It also sends an important message to teachers, in the light of research findings presented in Chapter 1 (Askew *et al*, 1997b) which suggests that effective teachers of numeracy emphasise interconnections between mathematical concepts. HMI explains the importance of the inter-relationship between concepts:

> No concept stands alone: for example, subtraction is linked with addition, multiplication is linked with addition and division, percentages are linked with fractions and decimals. In fact, each concept is linked with many other aspects of mathematics. . . Indeed, being 'good at mathematics' is dependant on the ability to recognise relationships between one concept and another. (p. 15)

Throughout the *Framework*, teachers are given suggestions as to how they can encourage children to make the inter-connections between concepts. Oral communication, emphasis on number properties, use of appropriate practical apparatus and discussions of algorithms and misconceptions are some of the strategies which will help children to build robust conceptual structures.

General strategies

These are related to strategies one uses for solving problems and carrying out investigations. When you are involved in problem-solving you will need to draw on three aspects of mathematical learning; knowledge of facts, appropriate skills and procedures, and problem-solving processes. When considering effective ways of teaching children to be numerate, it is important to consider what these processes are.

What are the processes which will support children to be successful problem solvers? The *Framework for teaching mathematics* 'integrates' the processes many of you have introduced as 'Using and Applying Mathematics' (usually known as Attainment Target 1) in the National Curriculum for mathematics (DfEE, 1995), which encourages three major strands:

◆ **making and monitoring decisions to solve problems** – this would involve the selection of appropriate materials, choice of methods and approaches;

◆ **developing mathematical communication** – this involves the development of mathematical language as well as oral and written communication of mathematics;

◆ **developing logic and reasoning** – this strand involves logical thinking and reasoning, making conjectures, proving and justifying methods.

The *Framework* emphasises the need for children to be able to select, communicate and justify methods and to develop estimation skills and ways to check results.

Personal qualities

Attitudes are important in all learning. Enjoyment and pleasure are, undoubtedly, contributing factors to all aspects of learning and the learning of mathematics is no exception. The fear, panic, anxiety and the feeling of inadequacy felt by many pupils and adults during their school days and beyond, is well documented. As positive attitudes can lead to success and more confidence, this is an aspect which needs careful consideration at the beginning of any new initiative. In this context, HMI's list of what encourages a positive attitude to learning mathematics (1985) is worthy of study. They are:

◆ fascination for the subject;

◆ interest and motivation;

◆ pleasure and enjoyment from mathematical activities;

◆ satisfaction derived from a sense of achievement;

◆ confidence in an ability to do mathematics at an appropriate level. (p. 25)

Teachers on our in-service courses have articulated that two aspects of the daily mathematics lesson have contributed to the development of positive attitudes: these are the 'increased level of opportunities to "talk" about mathematics' and the 'greater amount of teacher contact'. While I was researching for my Mental Mathematics books (Koshy, 1998) I spoke to many children who articulated their enjoyment of mental mathematics lessons. A fitting way to end this section may be to quote Patsy, age 6, who initiated the following conversation with some unsolicited remarks about mental maths, during one of my visits to her school:

P: *Do you know what we do every morning? We do mental number work. It is really good.*

V: *Tell me more about what you do in your mental number lesson.*

P: *It is really exciting, you have to add and take away numbers in your head. You are not allowed to use your fingers or anything like that.*

V: *So how do you do it, without using fingers?*

P: *Well, I know some of them anyway and if I don't use fingers, but I just look at my fingers without moving my head so my teacher doesn't see me using them. My target for this week is to think of 5 different ways of making 6 and say it in one breath.*

V: *Who set that target? I mean about the breath bit?*

P: *I did.*

V: *Have you learned them yet?*

P: *I am getting there, it is good you know . . .*

Effective teaching of number

In the previous section, I discussed features under five headings which contribute to acquiring good habits in learning mathematics. Both HMI advice and the principles set out in the National Numeracy Strategy guided my discussion. Before considering effective practical ways of teaching number to children, readers may find it useful to consider the following recommendations from the School Curriculum and Assessment Authority (1997):

Effective teaching of number should:

◆   find ways of helping pupils make connections between conceptual and calculational aspects of mathematics;

◆   provide opportunities for pupils to explain their mental processes and to know the methods that others use;

◆   encourage pupils to explain how they arrived at correct answers as well as incorrect ones;

◆   provide instruction in strategic approaches by 'modelling' strategies which feed in new ideas to build upon and extend pupils' methods, but not immediately expect pupils to adopt such methods;

◆ provide a range of models of the number system, including diagrams, measures and number lines as well as symbols and practical materials;

◆ carefully monitor the sense pupils make of models of the number system;

◆ treat calculations as problems requiring pupils to make sense of numbers and interpret them in a meaningful way, rather than simply trying to 'spot' the methods to apply;

◆ use 'realistic' contexts to help pupils both appreciate the application of number and provide a foundation for the introduction of new ideas.

As you unpack the requirements of teaching **number** in the Framework, you will see that the above principles are incorporated into the text.

From principles to practice

Having explored principles of teaching number, the next step is to consider aspects of practice. The Framework for teaching mathematics is presented as five strands as can be seen in Figure 2.1.

The first three strands: **Numbers and the number system, Calculations** and **Solving Problems**, deal with aspects of number and match the contents of the National Curriculum (QCA, 2000). There are many applications of number included in the other two strands; **Measures, Shape and Space** and **Handling Data**, which will contribute to the development of numeracy.

This chapter focuses on the elements of the first three strands of the Framework, which are directly related to teaching aspects of number. What I have included in this chapter are key issues from the three strands which I believe help children to develop a number sense. I have been helped by practising teachers in selecting the content.

To set the scene for the next section, let us take a quick look at the three strands. They highlight what I mentioned in Chapter 1; it is pleasing to see that 'being numerate' is interpreted differently to just doing sums and learning tables. Many other aspects of teaching number are recommended in the Framework, including the development of processes of problem-solving, which many of us have fought hard to include and then retain in the National Curriculum. Analysing the Framework further, we can identify some fundamental objectives being put forward for the effective teaching of 'number': **speed, efficiency, flexibility, understanding** and **application**.

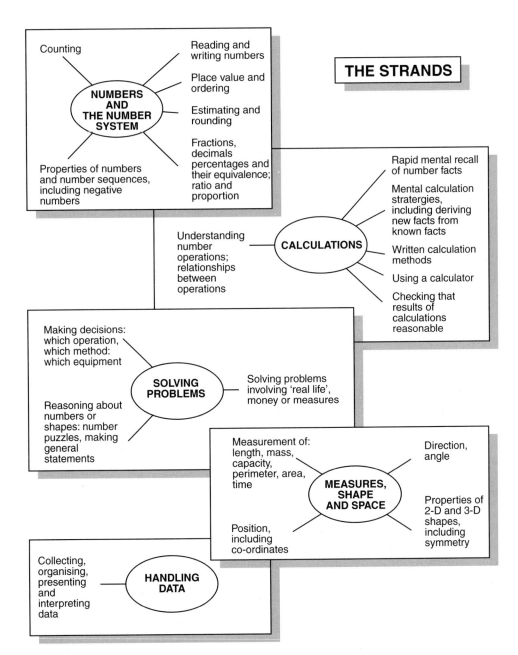

Figure 2.1 The 5 Framework strands

Developing children's number sense

Younger children learning about number

I watched a young child, Philip, aged five years and 7 months, who was asked by his teacher to count out six objects, put them on a tray and then write something and place what he had written next to the collection to show someone else how many there were. Philip counted one, two, three, four, five and six as he was picking up the objects and placed them on the tray. He stopped picking the objects up and said, 'it is six here now'. Then he took a piece of paper and wrote a 'very big' numeral 6 and smiled, expecting a big smile back from the teacher and from me in recognition of what he had achieved.

Natasha, aged five years and 6 months, was asked to do the same. She did not count one by one, but just took out three counters twice and placed them on the tray; she too wrote the numeral 6 to signpost the number in the set.

Think for a minute and list what Philip and Natasha 'knew' in order to be able to do what they have done.

> Philip knew how to count from one to six.
> He knew the number names from one to six.
> He knew that each new object corresponded to the next number name.
> He knew he had to stop when he got to number six.
> Philip could also write the number 6 correctly.

Natasha knew all that Philip knew, but it can be assumed that she also knew that a set of six is made up of two lots of threes.

Both children have acquired the skill of 'counting' and 'knowing number names' which are of fundamental importance in learning about number, whatever the stage of learning one is at. In Natasha's case, it may be that she has developed a conceptual understanding of what number six is made up of.

Although recent research literature on younger children's learning of mathematics is sparse, it is generally expected that young children need a variety of experiences of both counting and working with objects. Instead of colouring pictures of objects and counting them on paper, they need to move the objects round alongside counting number names. Counting can be learnt by rote and it may be tempting for both parents and teachers to have an exaggerated view of a children's understanding of number if they can count accurately. Practical work and discussion must supplement counting activities.

It is unlikely that young children learn about numbers in the order they appear on a number line. It is possible that they will learn about a number which they have used for a meaningful purpose. Therefore, to help their acquisition of number concepts you need to include activities which are set in familiar contexts or situations which are meaningful to them; stories, songs or games to name a few examples. I also think that it would be unwise to restrict younger children in learning only 'small' numbers until they are ready for larger numbers!

Exploring properties of numbers

Children of all ages are often fascinated to learn about the properties of numbers; they enjoy being taught about odd and even numbers, square numbers, cube numbers, factors, prime numbers and multiples. As these names and the associated concepts are mathematical, you need to use structured situations for children to grasp them. Effective teaching of these will also be enhanced by discussions, reinforcement in lessons and displays in the classroom. The two structured activities presented here have been selected because they have generated much enthusiasm amongst children and they were described as 'good' activities by teachers who tried them.

The ladybird problem

The ladybird problem presented below, from the ATM publication (1991) 'Exploring mathematics with younger children', shows how a group of six year-olds became familiar with the idea of *odd* and *even* numbers.

The ladybird needs to have the same number of spots on both sides.

Ask the children to investigate which numbers work.

Why doesn't number 1 work?

Why does number 2 work?

What about < 9? 102?

When children were told to work out what numbers the ladybird could use, the following responses came from the children:

◆   'every other number on the number line'

◆ 'you can't use the first number – one – you can use the next one, it looks like a pattern'

◆ 'numbers with a zero at the end seem to work'

At this point, the teacher joined the group and asked: 'do you know what the "yes" numbers are called?' One of the children, James, knew the answer and responded: 'they are even numbers'. 'What do we call the numbers which are not even numbers?'; 'odd numbers', James replied. A discussion followed as the teacher asked children to name other even numbers. A challenge to the concept of even numbers came when she asked: 'How do we describe an "even number"?' 'What is special about it?' The following conversation demonstrates the value of focused discussions:

Mandy: 'Even' numbers can be split into two.

Asha: (immediately challenging) 'All numbers can be split into two, you get two halves.'

Mandy: But the ladybird doesn't want half spots does he?

After more discussion it was decided that they would define 'even numbers' as numbers which can be split into two whole numbers.

Property boards

Another activity which can help children to consider properties of number was introduced by a Year 3 class teacher, Laura. She demonstrated how to play the game to the whole class using three volunteers, using property boards marked as shown opposite.

Each player was given a property board and a set of shuffled cards from a pack of 0–100 cards. With the whole class watching and listening, Laura explained to them that they must place the cards on the board in appropriate positions, in turn, with the objective of using up all the cards. The first person to use up all their cards wins the game. After the demonstration, groups of children were given 'property boards' of graded complexity – including 'square numbers', 'factors' 'divisibility statements' and 'prime numbers' – according to the experiences and abilities of the children. This kind of activity, if it is preceded and followed by discussion of properties of number, has high potential for contributing learning about numbers. It also provides the teacher with opportunities for assessing children's learning.

Using number lines

Whatever the size or nature of the numbers children are learning, a number line can be a very useful model. Children meet natural numbers 1, 2, 3 and 4 and so on first, and they learn that they go up in 'ones' on the number line. They will begin to realise that they can count on forever on a number line and also that there is a difference of one between consecutive numbers on a

Between 60 and 70	Odd	Multiple of 6	Has 3 as a factor
Less than 20	Prime number	Greater than 69	Even

Is in the x tables of 2 and 5	Multiple of 7	Has 2 as a factor	Prime number
Even	Both digits are odd	Greater than 29, less than 49	Odd

Greater than 35	Multiple of 3	Prime number	Odd
Has 4 as a factor	Even	Both digits are even	Between 29 and 59

Figure 2.2 Property boards

number line. The existence of a number line makes it possible for us to show how to order numbers according to size. Children can use number lines to learn to model 'addition' as counting on, 'subtraction' as counting back. They can multiply by modelling jumps on the number line and so on. A number line can also be used to show extensions to negative numbers when temperature needs to be recorded. Fraction and decimal number lines are necessary when you want to represent rational numbers (fractions). The types of number lines presented on page 26 show the potential for their use.

The use of number lines – both marked and blank – is suggested throughout the *Framework* to learn about whole numbers, fractions, decimals and negative numbers. I think that developing a mental number line is one of the strongest and most useful mental images in helping us to undertake mental calculations, ordering, estimating and rounding numbers.

Learning about place value

What is place value? The number system we use is based on the Hindu-Arabic place system in which all numbers can be represented using just 10 digits; 0, 1, 2, 3, 4, 5, 6, 7, 8, 9. The base 10 system, as it is referred to,

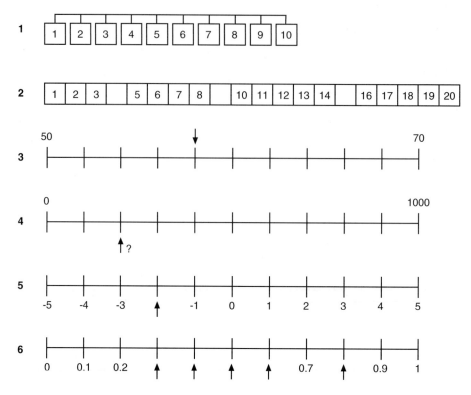

Figure 2.3 Number lines

may have something to do with us having ten fingers. Both larger and smaller numbers, whole numbers and decimals, can be constructed by using the same 10 digits, using powers of ten:

$$1000 = 10 \times 10 \times 10 = 10^3$$
$$100 = 10 \times 10 = 10^2$$
$$10 = 10 = 10^1$$
$$1 = 10^0$$
$$\frac{1}{10} = \frac{1}{10^1} = 10^{-1}$$
$$\frac{1}{100} = \frac{1}{10^2} = 10^{-2}$$
$$\frac{1}{1000} = \frac{1}{10^3} = 10^{-3}$$

What is involved in learning place value? A few years ago, as part of my research with 9 and 10 year-olds, I identified the following aspects as important teaching points for children to develop an understanding of place value (Koshy, 1988). They are given in Figure 2.4.

Aspect	Concepts/skills involved	Examples
Correspondence between name and place including zero as a place holder	The ability to write a correct sequence of digits corresponding to the name of a number	Write these numbers as figures: eighty three, two thousand and sixty three.
	Being able to understand the change in value when a digit in a specified position is changed	A second hand car had the following price label on it. £2560. One day the owner replaced the number 5 with a 3. What is the change in price?
	The ability to write a number in symbols from a concrete representation	Here is a collection of peppermints: 3 bags of hundreds and 6 tubes of tens. (Concrete materials were shown.) Can you write down, in figures, what the total number of peppermints is?
The grouping idea	Numbers are built on the grouping and regrouping of ones into tens, then into hundreds and so on	If I have 2556 sweets and I want to put them in bags of ten. How many bags can I make? What if I then decide to make up bags of hundreds. How many can I make?
Ordering of numbers	The ability to order a collection of numbers from largest to smallest	Arrange the following numbers in order, starting with the largest: 1001, 1200, 1100, 999, 1990.
The number line concept	The ability to judge which number is the nearest to a specified number on a number line	Which of the following numbers is nearest to 478: 578, 399, 500, 408?
The scale factor idea	The ability to recognise that each place value is worth 10 times the place value to its right	I have 60 marbles, my friend has 600 marbles. How many times bigger is my friend's number?

Figure 2.4 An analysis of concepts and skills involved in teaching place value

The importance of place value is emphasised in the *Framework* and this aspect of learning number is given prominence in the Numeracy Strategy. As our number system is based on a rule which assigns values to digits by virtue of their position, it is reasonable to assert here that a robust understanding of the place value principles is needed for carrying out number operations efficiently, with both whole numbers and decimals as well as being able to estimate. As most of you know, many of children's mistakes and misconceptions originate from a lack of understanding of the principles of place value.

How can we develop children's understanding of place value?

Using practical apparatus

With younger children you could do the following activities which involve grouping in tens. It is important to use different materials and ask questions which highlight the grouping aspect. Although the following activities themselves may be familiar to you, I have presented them in a way which emphasises the objectives of conceptual understanding, discussion and learning of correct mathematics vocabulary.

Handful – a grouping game

Demonstrate the game with two or more children playing. Tell the children that in this activity they will be grouping things into tens. Each player picks up one handful of unifix, centicubes or matchsticks. Each handful is then to be put into sets of tens (others can help with this) – as ten sticks in the case of unifix or centicubes or as bundles of ten if you are using matchsticks. Fill in the score sheet each round. Play this a few rounds.

Handfuls	Player 1		Player 2	
	t	u	t	u
1st handful				
2nd handful				
3rd handful				

When children are making tens and writing the scores down, let them explain what they are doing emphasising the fact that they are recording the 'tens and ones' as we normally write two-digit numbers.

Using Dienes blocks

Practical *structured* apparatus modelling the place value system is often used to explain place value principles to children. The materials commonly used in schools are called Dienes blocks, named after Z.P. Dienes who developed the idea of multibase blocks. The following model shows base ten materials grouped as hundreds, tens and ones.

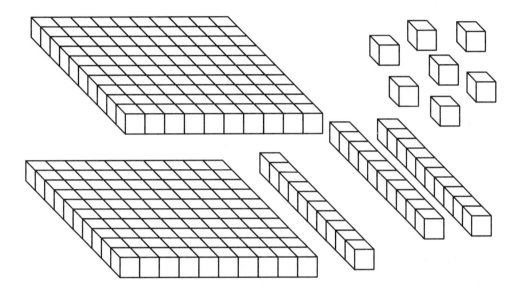

The idea of place value is complex; children need to spend time internalising this concept. They need to acquire an understanding of the equivalence of ten ones or units to one ten and ten tens to one hundred and so on. Most of you must be familiar with place value activities; what is important is the way in which we introduce them and help children to make connections between the concrete materials and the abstract ideas presented. Suppose you are using the following two activities with your class:

Target 30 – a place value game

Up to four people can play this game. It is useful to demonstrate it to the whole class to facilitate discussion and the correct use of vocabulary.

You need: *a collection of Dienes blocks (hundreds, tens and units), a place value board for each player, one die marked 1 to 6*

Take turns to roll the die. Collect that number of ones or units and place them on your board where 'units' or 'ones' is marked. When you have collected ten or more ones in your units column, exchange them for a ten. For example if you have 12 units, you would exchange them for 1 ten block and leave the 2 units in the units column. Keep playing until one of the players has collected 3 tens which is the target.

tens	ones

hundreds	tens	ones

Using number cards or dice with bigger numbers, you can choose higher targets involving hundreds.

Race to zero

This is the reverse of the 'Target' game. You need the same materials.

Start with 3 ten blocks in the tens column and use the reverse process. Both players start with 3 tens. They take turns to throw the die and take away the number 'thrown' away from the total, exchanging the tens for ones when necessary. My own research pointed out that when children kept recordings of their running totals as the game progressed they were making connections between the recording of tens and units and the model blocks. For example, on his score sheet, player 1 may record

$$
\begin{array}{l}
30-5 \\
25-6 \\
19-3 \\
16-4 \\
12-1 \\
11-5 \\
6-6 \\
0.
\end{array}
$$

as he gets rid of his blocks.

Of course, this game may also be a familiar to you; but the reason for including it is to emphasise some important points to remember when using concrete representations of a number. These points are useful to bear in mind when using any practical activities:

◆ In the past, many of these activities may have been used in small groups, with the teacher explaining the rules to each group and allowing extended time for playing them. Within the structure of the daily mathematics lessons, these games could be used as class demonstration activities with volunteers playing them in front of the class. This not only saves teacher time, but it also enables the teacher to focus questions, discuss pupil responses on the principles of place value and monitor the use of correct vocabulary.

◆ Research has pointed out (Hart *et al*, 1989)) that practical apparatus alone does not contribute to an understanding of mathematical ideas; teacher discussion plays an important part.

Highest, lowest, nearest – for teaching place value and ordering

This game can be played by up to four players. If it is a whole-class lesson, others can watch.

You need: *place value boards for each of the players marked units, tens and hundreds and a few sets of 0 to 9 cards placed face down.*

Decide first whether your target is to make the highest, lowest or the nearest to a specified number. Say you chose 'highest'. Take turns to pick a card and place it in a position on the board. Once it is placed, it cannot be moved. During the next round a second card is placed in one of the remaining spaces, and so on. The person who makes the highest number wins.

Again, the game itself may be familiar to you. It will be worth spending a little time to write a list of the objectives for this activity: The list may include the following:

◆ *reading and recognising number names,*

◆ *ordering numbers,*

◆ *understanding and awareness of the value of the digit being determined by the position it occupies on the board.*

When you play for the 'nearest' version of the game, the concepts of a number line and the process of rounding are also being highlighted. Having these objectives written down, at the beginning of the lesson, will help you to target questions and explanations during the activity.

Using number arrow cards

Arrow cards are ingenious devices to show how the grouping rule of the place value system works. They reinforce the idea that a number such as 349, is made up of separate components: 3 stands for 300, 4 stands for 40 and the 9 stands for 9 units or ones.

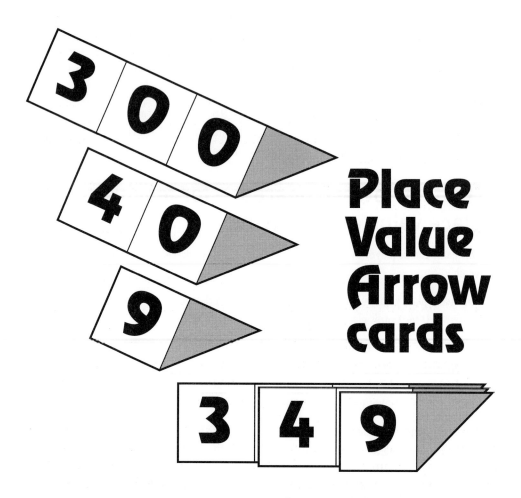

As you can see, the arrow cards show the components of a number which can then be shown by overlapping the cards in the appropriate way. As in the case of number lines these cards can help children to understand the place value structure as well as help them to develop efficient calculation strategies. One pack of arrow cards consists of 9 cards of hundreds (100–900) 9 cards of tens (10–90) and 9 cards from 1 to 9. You would need several packs of these in order to use them for whole class lessons.

As with all practical apparatus, the success of using arrow cards will really depend on the type and range of questions asked by the teacher. The following questions may exemplify some of the ideas you can address using arrow cards. Many of these ideas can be used with the whole class, providing opportunities for differentiated questioning.

◆ Make the numbers: 28, 31, 20, 256, 350, 507. It is important to emphasise the role of zero as a place holder. Let children experience that they only need two cards 500 and 7 to make the number 507.

◆ Show me a 2-digit number with three tens, a 3-digit number with a zero in the middle, a 3-digit number with 2 zeros. Make a number with all the 3 digits the same. How do you read that number? Get children to read numbers aloud.

◆ Make a number with 4 tens, say, 45. Show me the number which is 3 more than that number, 6 more, 10 more and so on. With 3 digit numbers: Show me a number with a zero in the ones column; what is 4 tens more than that number?

◆ Make a number between 50 and 90. Say 76 was made. What do we call that number?

◆ Make a number bigger than 359; make a number between 250 and 569.

◆ Make a 3-digit number; add a ten to it, add a hundred, add 300.

◆ With the whole class watching, let a group of four children pick up any three cards each – you could make it one of each, if you prefer – ones, tens or hundreds. Ask them to make: the largest number possible, smallest number, a number less than a given number, a number which is the nearest to a given number and so on. Let all children participate in discussing the results.

Whilst in the past the kind of activities I have presented above may have been done in small groups, in the context of the interactive, whole class teaching style recommended in the National Numeracy Strategy, it would make sense to demonstrate the ideas to the whole class with all children participating in the discussions.

The importance of understanding place value

As I have mentioned earlier, a good understanding of place value is vital for children to develop the necessary skills for carrying out both mental and written calculations. It also provides them with a sound basis for extending their work from natural numbers to decimal numbers. So, naturally, the next question to consider is: what does research say about children's understanding of place value?

There is evidence (Brown, 1981; Koshy, 1988; SCAA, 1997) to show that children at all Key Stages experience difficulties with some aspects of place value. Difficulties are often associated with reading and writing large numbers, using zero as place holder, and when using place value principles in applying rules for number operations. In fact, many children's mistakes arise from a faulty or partial understanding of the place value concept.

One possible reason, suggested by SCAA, (1997) for younger children's difficulty in internalising the principle of place value is the nature of the number names between 10 and 59. The reason for Japanese children acquiring a greater understanding of place value is explained in terms of the Japanese number system having number names up to hundreds, 'consistent with the numbers they represent' – e.g. twenty two contains 2 tens 2. It is suggested that in the 'English system, the naming of numbers in relation to their place value does not begin to appear until numbers containing hundreds', e.g. three hundred and twenty nine. Restricting young pupils to smaller numbers may be doing them a disservice because it is not 'until one gets into "sixties" that the place value and number names come together: six-ty, seven-ty eigh(t)y and nine-ty. Twenty and thirty instead of two-ty and three-ty do not make the structure explicit'.

Extending place value to decimals

Decimal numbers constitute an extension of the natural number system to include fractional parts. When children appreciate that numbers are made of digits and the position of the digit determines its value, they can be shown that the principle remains the same as digits continue to occupy positions to the right of the units and are referred to as tenths, hundredths, thousandths and so on. The positions to the right are called *decimal places* and the *decimal point* separates whole numbers from fractional parts, based on multiples of ten.

The important role of zero as a place holder needs to be stressed again in the context of decimal numbers. Ask children to imagine if someone paid them £54 rather than £504. In the same way ask them which would they rather have: 0.9 or 0.009, of a bar of their favourite chocolate.

As in the case of whole numbers, the introduction to decimal numbers also needs to be thorough. Use of structured apparatus, calculators and decimal number lines alongside discussion of principles, should continue as long as they are needed.

Research has pointed out that the concept of decimals is found difficult by children well into their secondary school careers. The two common errors made by children working with decimals, explained by Askew (1997), provide considerable insight into what we may need to address while teaching decimals.

The two errors – DPI error (Decimal Points Ignored) and LS error (Largest is Smallest) – were highlighted during tests given to 150 000 11 to 15 year-olds by the Assessment of Performance Unit (APU). The DPI error occurs when children ignore the decimal points in numbers and treat them as whole numbers. For example, when they are asked to order 0.07, 0.23, 0.1 from smallest to largest 31% of 11 year-olds gave the answer 0.1, 0.07, 0.23. The LS error occurs when children think that the size of a decimal is related to the number of decimal places a number has, the more decimal places it has the smaller it is. In Askew's specific example, many children considered 0.475 to be smaller than 0.33. Perhaps we need to re-examine the way we explain the role of the decimal point to children to see if explanations such as a 'decimal point makes the number smaller' contribute to this misconception.

During a whole class lesson, you may want to ask different children to tell you which of the two numbers – 12.4 or 12.35 – is bigger and give you an explanation, justifying their decision. It should provide you with very useful information about their level of understanding.

Highs and Lows – a decimal game

Using structured activities, such as the 'Highs and Lows' (Koshy, 1998) cited below, is an excellent way of generating discussion of principles and exposing misconceptions. I have observed a Year 6 class playing this game as part of their daily mathematics lesson. To play 'Highs and Lows' you need place value boards marked with decimal points, units, tens and hundreds and tenths and hundredths as shown below. You also need sets of 0–9 cards.

h	t	u	$\cdot \dfrac{1}{10}$	$\dfrac{1}{100}$

Before the game starts, you need to choose your criterion for winning – whether to make the lowest or biggest number obtained decide the winner. Each player chooses a card, in turn, and places it in a position on the board bearing in mind the 'highest or lowest' criterion selected. The person whose number fulfils the criterion wins that round.

In the lesson I observed, the teacher selected a group of three children to play the game whilst the others watched. She asked the children to explain why they chose the positions they did to place the cards. Both the level of questioning and making the children explain what they were doing were impressive. She drew out many place value principles during that short demonstration: the importance of where you place a digit, the role of the decimal point, the effect a decimal point has on the size of a number and so on.

Learning about fractions and percentages

Placing this section after decimals does not suggest that one should teach these topics in that order. It seems to make sense to introduce decimals straight after discussing place value. In fact, I would expect children to have some knowledge of the concept of fractions before they are introduced to the idea of 'tenths' and 'hundredths' in the decimal system.

Children experience many difficulties and misconceptions in dealing with fractions. In a small project (with Year 6 classes) I carried out with the help of teachers who attend our in-service programmes, we tried to highlight some of the difficulties experienced by children in dealing with fractions. Then we tried to think about ways in which these difficulties can be alleviated through the teaching programme. The following were our findings:

◆ Most children seemed to have developed a concept of fractions which only dealt with a 'whole' something – apple, squared paper or chocolate – being cut into equal parts. This created problems for them when questions such as: what is $\frac{1}{5}$ of 90, or $\frac{1}{8}$ of 816 had to be dealt with. The question: what is $\frac{3}{8}$ of £32.16 was found to be even more difficult as many of them tried to figure out whether you divide by 8 or 3 first. Taking note of the difficulties experienced by the children, some of the course members decided to re-visit or re-teach fractions. David, one of the teachers who retaught his children the concept of fractions, shared with us a child's entry in his 'glossary' book, which showed that he had developed a different concept of a fraction to what he had originally expressed – 'as a part of one whole' (see opposite).

◆ Many of the children found the idea of equivalent fractions difficult. Teachers felt this concept needs more teacher input and discussion than they had originally thought. The speculation was that children who add tops and bottoms when they had to add the two fractions $\frac{1}{4} + \frac{1}{3} = \frac{2}{7}$ may be doing so after failing to recall how they could make 'the bottom two numbers' the same.

Fraction number lines proved particularly useful in developing a conceptual

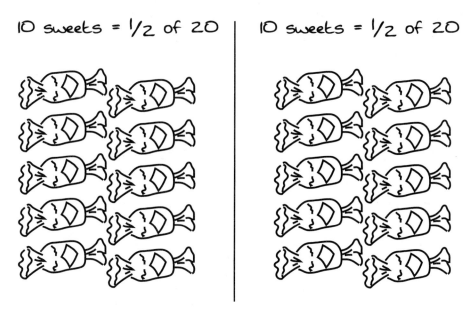

10 sweets = 1/2 of 20 | 10 sweets = 1/2 of 20

20 sweets is shared amongst 2 people
that means each person gets 10 sweets
because 10 × 2 = 20 = 10 = 1/2 of 20

understanding of fractions and their relative sizes. Working with blank 'fraction' number lines proved useful in reducing mistakes.

Making links between fractions, decimals and percentages

It is a good idea to link fractions, decimals and percentages. Games such as 'snap' offer structured opportunities for doing this. To make a snap game

---

'Percentage fortune'

A simple game – I called it 'Percentage fortune' – asking children to collect money using 2 dice. One die marked with mixed representations on all the 6 sides, say, 25%, $\frac{1}{3}$, 0.75, 20%, 0.5, $\frac{1}{4}$ and the other die marked with an amount, say, £125, £160, £50, £500, £350 and £30. Roll the two dice together and collect the appropriate amount, such as 20% of £350, keeping a running total. The person with the highest total wins.

Games such as the one described above are easy to design and adapt. Again, what is important is the level of interaction in the lesson which encourages children to explain their methods and justify their decisions.

you need to make a few sets of cards which show representations of all three – fractions, decimals and percentages. For example, a set of matching cards will consist of 0.5, $\frac{1}{2}$, 50%, $\frac{4}{8}$ and so on. Charts such as the one below could be used to show equivalence:

Fraction	Decimal	Percentage
$\frac{1}{4}$	0.25	25%
$\frac{1}{5}$	0.20	20%
$\frac{1}{2}$	0.50	50%
$\frac{1}{3}$	0.33	33%
$\frac{1}{10}$	0.10	10%
$\frac{11}{20}$	0.55	55%
$\frac{37}{50}$	0.74	74%
$\frac{1}{8}$	0.125	$12\frac{1}{2}$%

Learning to estimate

Dianne, aged ten, was working out a problem using a calculator. She suddenly stopped and said: 'Blow it, it must be the calculator'. I got interested and asked her why she was getting agitated. She explained:

> It must be the calculator, no way would I get an answer like that. I must have pressed the wrong key or something like that. I never trust a calculator. When I use a calculator I always try to have an idea what the answer is going to be like.

I was very reassured by these comments and wish all our children had as much confidence in their numerical ability as Dianne did.

Estimation in this instance is having a rough idea about what the answer is going to be like. Our ability to estimate is enhanced by two factors: being able to think in our heads and having a good understanding of how numbers behave. Many of the activities I have included in this book encourage estimating. My own belief is that if we ask children, periodically, to estimate the answers and write them down before they actually carry out calculations or solve problems, the number of mistakes they make could be greatly reduced.

Developing an understanding of calculations

A numerate person will be able to carry out calculations efficiently and accurately and with a good degree of confidence, no matter how the data are presented. So, it is reasonable to assume that a numerate person would possess some or all of the following attributes:

◆ a good understanding of the number system;

◆ an understanding of the basic number operations and the relationship between them;

◆ a set of sound strategies for mental calculations;

◆ flexibility in the choice of what procedures to use;

◆ the ability to make sense of the results of the calculations;

◆ the ability to spot unreasonable solutions.

Although the National Curriculum emphasises that all these should be addressed in mathematics lessons, there is evidence from Ofsted reports that in many classrooms there is excessive reliance on written methods of calculations, often due to commercially produced text books. I observed two examples which showed that children were more interested in conforming to text book methods and what they thought was expected of them by their teacher.

Melanie, aged nine, copied out and performed the operation with many crossings out, as can be seen.

$$
\begin{array}{r}
{}^1\!\!\!\not4\ {}^1\!\not0\ {}^1\!\not0\ 0\ - \\
6 \\
\hline
1\ 1\ 1\ 4 \\
\hline
\end{array}
$$

I asked Melanie to look at her sum and explain to me how she had done it. Within a few seconds, Melanie responded: 'O, my God. It isn't right, is it?' – She said she knew what 4000 take away 6 was; and gave me the correct answer of 3994. Then she explained: it was just that she couldn't remember which numbers to cross out. I asked her why she did not just write the correct answer and not bother with all the crossings out. Melanie was insistent that her teacher would be cross with her for ignoring her instructions. I decided not to discuss this with the teacher for obvious reasons.

The second experience was similar. Here Ben, also nine years old, was doing a page of addition sums from a text book. The whole set of sums, 14 in total, were written horizontally, for example:

234 + 67 + 387 =
1234 + 345 + 9 = and so on

I saw Ben writing correct answers on a piece of scrap paper and then presenting each sum in his mathematics book. In his book, he had presented them vertically and neatly; he had remembered (correctly!) how to carry tens and hundreds. When I asked him what he was doing, he responded that he did the sums mentally first to make sure they were all right before recording them the way he was supposed to.

One of the main aims of the Numeracy Strategy is to offer children the flexibility to calculate using the most effective strategies at their disposal at any given time. Few people will disagree with this objective, although I feel we need to rethink our current methods of teaching calculations and refine our teaching strategies.

So where do we start? First, consider the recommendations of the National Numeracy Strategy; there is a strong emphasis on mental calculations; the *Framework* also asserts that 'an ability to calculate mentally lies at the heart of numeracy'. A close look at the sections on mental calculations in the *Framework* will show that mental methods are defined quite broadly. Mental calculations are not just about learning and remembering facts, but also about deriving new facts from known facts. Estimating, reasoning, checking and convincing all play a part in being good at mental arithmetic. It is not assumed that children will acquire mental calculation skills automatically, they need to be taught how to develop these strategies. As the whole of Chapter 3 of this book is devoted to mental mathematics, this aspect is not dealt with in more detail here.

When you read the section on calculations in the *Framework*, some clear philosophies and principles emerge. A progression in teaching calculations is also suggested:

◆ During the first few years of schooling children are encouraged to develop mental strategies. They will count objects, learn number names, the ordinal and cardinal aspects of number. Through practical activities and discussion children, at this stage, will acquire an understanding of number bonds and number operations.

◆ As children develop confidence in using mental methods, they will be introduced to larger numbers, place value ideas and what is involved in number operations. Recording will be flexible and according to what the child's personal needs are.

◆ Formal recording is delayed until children are in Year 3, this is justified in terms of the fact that in many countries which performed well in the international mathematics tests children are involved in a great deal of oral and mental work before formal recording.

◆ Standard algorithms are introduced gradually, whilst encouraging children to use mental calculations wherever possible.

◆ Calculators are introduced in Year 5 and children are taught how to use them efficiently and sensibly.

Teaching addition and subtraction

The following practical ideas are effective in developing an understanding of the operations of addition and subtraction:

◆ Get children to talk about sets of objects such as beads, pennies, dice, feely bags and talk about more and less.

◆ Count on and back with number lines, rhymes and track games.

◆ Explore different ways of making numbers; 5, 6 and 10 and memorise number bonds.

◆ Practise counting and realise that you can start from the first number in the first set and not count both sets.

◆ Hide objects from a set and find the missing number.

◆ Make up and tell number sentences and statements for both + and − using real examples and stories.

◆ Discuss that $3 + 4$ is the same as $4 + 3$ according to the commutative principle, and that $4 − 3$ is not the same as $3 − 4$.

◆ Ask word problems: Using two/three dice how many ways can you make 10? 12?

◆ What is 4 more than 9?

◆ In how many different ways can you break a 10 stick of unifix? What is the difference between the two sticks each time?

◆ Add a string of numbers and discuss how the order in which the numbers are added does not change the answer.

◆ Use place value principles to add and subtract numbers.

◆ Use a number line to add and subtract numbers, discuss strategies.

◆ Make flexible recordings of addition and subtraction.

◆ Discuss with other people how they calculate.

Teaching multiplication and division

◆ Counting in groups of 2, 3, 4 or 10 using fingers, feet and toes with committing to memory as an objective.

◆ Patterns on number lines, number squares, pegs and unifix sticks.

◆ Number games and activities for moving forward and back. 'Freddie the frog is standing on number 4, he is jumping in 4s, can you tell him where to go next?'

◆ Practical sharing activities with accompanying discussion: 12 smarties are shared between 3 children; they have 4 each, then try sharing among 4 children, then 5 generating remainders.

◆ Play 'Handfuls': take a handful of beans and ask children to predict if it is an even number, odd number, whether it can be shared into 3, 4, 5 and so on.

◆ Play circle games: Fizz-buzz, chanting tables, generate times tables on a spreadsheet.

◆ Solve word problems which involve multiplication and division, including division with remainders.

◆ Discuss the need to round up or down according to context: If 35 people can travel on a bus and 360 people have to travel, you need 11 buses – not 10 buses with 10 as remainder.

◆ Play grab (see Chapter 4).

◆ Introduce the ideas of factors, multiples and so on. Play 'guess my number' from clues and similar oral games.

◆ Multiply a 2-digit number by a 1-digit number:
$47 \times 6 = (40 + 7) \times 6 = 40 \times 6 + 7 \times 6$; explaining the
distributive law.

Understanding operations

The key to children understanding number operations is the way in which
they make sense of the principles behind an operation, as well as the inter-
connections between operations. For example, after solving a word problem:
Janet has 45 marbles, James has 55, how many more marbles has James got?
A child who has worked it out as $45 + 10 = 55$ and gives the answer 10,
may quite reasonably be confused if the teacher expected that child to have
performed a subtraction. Therefore, discussions of how addition is related to
subtraction, how multiplication can be seen as repeated addition and
division as repeated subtraction are very useful indeed.

Another important point to remember is to present number operations in
many different ways, using them in both realistic contexts and structured
situations. It would be useful for children to record the operation they have
carried out for different situations and different types of word problems.
Number stories are always very useful for this purpose. We all know that, to
a child who is very proficient in adding numbers with examples, an
operation such as $6 + 3 = 9$ or $4 + 3 = 7$, can be very confusing when
expressed in a different way: $6 + \square = 9$ or $\square + 3 = 7$.

Whatever the operation being introduced or being practised, we need to
make sure that children are taught the most effective strategies to use. I have
often observed how children who use very laborious methods of calculation
appreciate being told or shown a more efficient method of calculation. One
example that comes to mind is when a child was struggling to add eight 'six
times' to answer the question: If each packet contains 8 sweets and you have
6 packets, how many sweets are there altogether? She was asked to think of
other ways of working it out, and was made to see that she could use the
times table fact 8×6 (which she knew) to get the answer!

Alphabet's worth

Recently I saw a group of 30 Year 2 children engaged in an activity called 'Alphabet's
worth', during an oral maths session.

To create a motivating context for practising the addition operation, the teacher told them
that they were going to give values to the letters of the alphabet: $A = 1$; $B = 2$; $C = 3$;
$Z = 26$ and so on. The objective of the lesson was to discuss a range of strategies to add a
string of numbers, thinking of differences and estimating. The teacher asked the children

how they would work out what a word was worth: DOG = 4 + 15 + 7 = 26 and then she asked everyone to work out what a CAT was worth. She asked one child to come and write the numbers 3 + 1 + 10 = on the board. Everyone performed the addition. Then came an interesting and very illuminating discussion on how different children worked the sums out. The relative merits of their methods were discussed, sensitively. Two principles were highlighted: the order in which you add numbers does not make a difference to the answer and that it is in fact a good idea to sometimes rearrange numbers to make it easier. Other questions asked during the session were:

- ◆ *Can you think of an animal which is worth at least 100?*

- ◆ *Which is worth more BANANA or PEAR?*

- ◆ *Can you work out whether a BAT is worth more than an ANT?*

A very lively and purposeful 10 minute session.

Learning written methods of calculations

On the first day of our in-service courses, we often get teachers to do a mental arithmetic activity. Teachers work in pairs asking each other questions which their partner has to work out mentally. By probing they find out how the partner worked out the answers. Although this activity generates a significant amount of stress initially, course members have always seen the usefulness and relevance of this exercise for their teaching. One of the questions we use for this exercise is a subtraction question: What is 212 take away 178? After everyone has finished, we discuss the methods used by everyone to work out this question.

During the discussions it usually emerges that a variety of methods have been used; the following are among the main strategies used to work out 212 take away 178:

- ◆ Most people use a number line strategy, which involves counting on or knowing that from 78, it is 22 more to 200, then add on 12 to make 34.

- ◆ Sometimes teachers describe 'seeing' (in their heads) the two numbers written vertically as a sum and they do it by crossing out numbers as one would do with a written algorithm.

- ◆ Occasionally, one or two people see the two numbers written as a vertical sum and try to use the 'borrowing' and 'paying back' method which they were taught. This leads to other members becoming both interested and confused because it is difficult to explain this method sensibly to someone else.

◆ Other 'personalised' methods were used; those who listened sometimes found it difficult to comprehend the ideas behind others' explanations and asked many challenging questions.

Regardless of the number of methods used, teachers have often been surprised by the variety of methods used for the same calculation and the fact that many of them resorted to a different way of doing the calculation because paper and pencil were not available. Another point that is usually raised by teachers is that it is difficult to carry out a calculation which involves larger numbers, mentally, using a method which is quite adequate for calculating smaller numbers. For example, if asked to take away 4567 from 9535; it was felt you either need to use paper and pencil or at least use a mental image of a vertical sum and all the crossings out. There is much food for thought here. Perhaps you could try a similar exercise with your children.

Standard written methods

Traditional written methods of calculations are taught in many schools and these are included in the *Framework*. Written calculations are more generalisable and, if performed correctly, give correct answers. Many children and adults feel secure knowing a commonly accepted algorithm for carrying out a specific calculation. Many children are shown how to perform standard calculations by their parents. It makes sense to encourage children to carry out mental calculations when they can, but also to teach them the traditional written methods.

Perhaps the best strategy to adopt is to encourage children to use the most efficient method for the task in hand. I showed previously how Melanie tried to subtract 6 from 4000 and got into a muddle with all the crossings out; the subsequent discussion with her showed that she knew the answer anyway! Here the vertical standard method actually got in the way of Melanie performing a calculation correctly. The traditional or standard way in which we do the four operations is given in Figure 2.5.

It is useful for teachers to adopt a consistent approach to written methods of calculation and to share these with both parents and secondary schools. I will conclude this section with what Lynne, a Year 6 teacher, told me:

After referring to the mathematics Framework, I asked my children to do some calculations. I told them that on that particular day they were going to do the sums without writing them down vertically. They were working in groups and as always were allowed to discuss what they were doing. They were asked to think about what they were doing and later make some comments about what they had done.

A selection of what the children did is shown below.

Victoria   20.3.99

1. 286−98

188 ✓
I did 286−100 which makes 186. I then added on 2 to make 188. That was my answer.

2.   4000−38

3962 ✓
I did 4000 take 40 to get, ~~3960~~ 3960. I then added on 2 to make 3962. That was my answer.

Suzanne
Ip.e.
20.3.99

1. 286−98 =   188 ✓

I took 90 from 280, the answer was 196, then I took 8 from 796 giving me the answer of the whole sum.

2. 4000−38 = 3962 ✓

I made 38, 40 and I took 40 from 4000 giving me 3960 then I added 2, giving me a total of 3962, that was the answer.

Sam

286−98 = 188
98 to 100 = 2
286−100 = (186 + 2) = 188

4000 − 38 = 3962
38 to 40 = 2
4000 − 40 = 3960 + 2 = 3962

Addition

You write the digits in the right columns and add from the units, carrying
tens and hundreds to the appropriate columns:

$$
\begin{array}{r}
2\ 7\ 9 \\
4\ 6\ 7 \\
\hline
7\ 4\ 6 \\
1\ 1
\end{array}
$$

Subtraction

The digits are written in columns and the process of decomposition is used,
the small numbers transferred are due to the process of exchange rather than
'borrow' because we don't 'pay back':

$$
\begin{array}{r}
^5\!6\ ^1\!4\ 8 \\
-\ 3\ 9\ 2 \\
\hline
2\ 2\ 6
\end{array}
$$

Multiplication

Short multiplication:

$$
\begin{array}{r}
3\ 4\ 7 \\
\times\quad 6 \\
\hline
2\ 0\ 8\ 2 \\
2\ 4
\end{array}
$$

Long multiplication – this varies; depending on whether you start
multiplying with the tens or units:

$$
\begin{array}{r}
3\ 8 \\
\times\quad 5\ 6 \\
\hline
1\ 9\ 0\ 0 \\
2\ 2\ 8 \\
\hline
2\ 1\ 2\ 8
\end{array}
$$

Division

Short division:

$$
6\overline{\smash{)}3\ 7^1\!8} = 63
$$

Long division:

$$
\begin{array}{r}
1\ 2\ 5 \\
21\overline{)2\ 6\ 2\ 5} \\
2\ 1 \\
\hline
5\ 2 \\
4\ 2 \\
\hline
1\ 0\ 5 \\
1\ 0\ 5
\end{array}
$$

Figure 2.5 Traditional written methods of calculations

The teacher made the following comments:

◆ Children found it very difficult to get started. They seemed lost; perhaps I had conditioned them too much to do sums all the time.

◆ Once they got started they seemed to enjoy themselves.

◆ Usually they work quietly getting on with the sums; that day they talked to each other a lot more, mostly about their work.

◆ The number of mistakes was certainly less.

These points certainly give us something to think about.

Solving problems

So far we have been concerned with children learning about the number system, properties of number and ways of calculating. Solving problems can be described as using and applying what has been learnt about number. In this respect, whilst solving problems, children will have plenty of opportunities to *use and apply* mathematics which the *Framework* refers to as permeating the whole teaching programme. Statements describing problem-solving processes – making decisions, justifying, generalising, proving, communicating and reasoning – appear throughout the section on solving problems in the *Framework*. There is little doubt that the ability to solve problems confidently and effectively contributes to raising achievement in mathematics. A close look at the Standard Assessment Tasks will show that all the skills being tested cannot be learnt by rote. Children are also asked to reason, identify patterns and provide explanations.

Having established that being able to solve problems is an important part of being numerate, let us now consider the types of problem-solving we see in classrooms.

Word problems which follow operations

Many text books provide problem-solving exercises at the end of a section dealing with a specific operation. For example, the following are the type of problems often included at the end of the section on addition:

John had 4 marbles, he won 7 more. How many has he now?

We have 12 writing books, 6 maths books and 13 word books. How many books are there altogether?

Naomi had 34 stamps in one packet and 23 in another. How many does she have altogether?

After the section on subtraction sums the same text book would have:

> I had 12 sweets, I ate 6. How many have I left?
>
> There are 24 children in the class, 7 are away. How many children are present?
>
> Out of the 16 children who went to a concert, 4 were girls, how many were boys?

It is unlikely that any child who works through these problems will have a problem deciding which operation to use. I heard someone once say that, even if the problems were written in another language, as long as the numbers were recognisable, children would get correct answers. Although it is important to be able to make decisions about what operation to use, it is unlikely that the above examples of problem-solving, in that particular setting, would help to develop that skill.

I have observed children use another method for deciding what operation to use to solve a word problem, which, again is unlikely to develop their numerical competence. This involves children looking for 'clue words' in the problem to help them to select the appropriate operation. For example, if the word 'more' appears in the problem, it is considered an addition operation, 'share' being the clue for 'division' and so on. I was once told by a child who had solved the problem: 'John had 46 marbles, Nadia had 58 marbles, how many more marbles did Nadia have than John?' that the answer could be found by adding the two numbers. Misleading clues lead children to make mistakes. It may be useful to be proactive in this context and give children clues which they may misunderstand, then discuss them, if only just to make a point.

Here are some examples of misleading clues in word problems. You may want to try this kind of problems with your children.

> Daniel has 8 cakes. He divided each cake into 4 pieces. How many pieces are there altogether?
>
> Ron has saved up £6 to buy a game. The game costs £15. How much more does he need?
>
> I have 16 stamps, My friend has 3 times as many. How many stamps do we have altogether?

Indeed, children need to spot what operations to use for solving word problems; but they need to make their decisions based on an understanding of what different operations are about. They need to make sense of the operations and what operations actually do to numbers. When asked, 'if one bag contains 8 sweets and you had 6 bags of them, how many are there altogether?' a child may start adding 8 six times. Here the teacher needs to point out the fact that multiplication is in fact repeated addition which would result in that child internalising that principle and applying it in future situations.

In the Framework, you are encouraged to engage children in different types of problem-solving activities. We have dealt with the type of problems which require selection of particular operations or a mixture of operations.

The problem-solving strand in the Framework includes two other types of problems – those which are purely mathematical and those which are realistic. Try solving this problem:

> If all 16 people in a room shook hands with each other once, how many handshakes will take place? What if there are 100 people? 1000 people? Can you work out a way of finding out the number of handshakes for any number of people?

The handshakes problem does not have a purpose in a real life context, but it provides an opportunity to work systematically, look for patterns and generalise. Any formulas arrived at may be useful in other similar situations which often gives children a kind of power.

Here is another problem which leads to a simple generalisation:

> Look at the way this pattern is made. In diagram number 1, two plain tiles are surrounded by some shaded tiles. In diagram number 2, three tiles are surrounded by shaded tiles. Can you predict the number of tiles needed to build a surround for 4 tiles, 5 tiles, for any number of tiles?

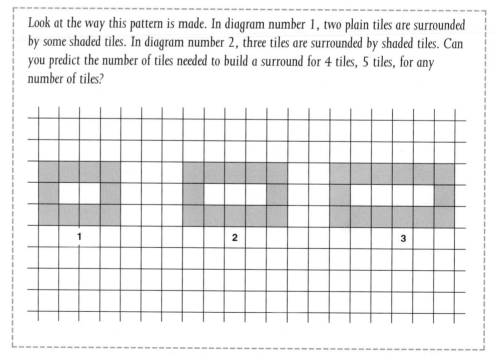

Some problems require the formation of an equation. For example, if I am asked the question 'think of a number, add 3, then multiply by 6 and tell me the answer' it requires me to work out the original number from the information I have. If the answer was 36, I need to know that I need to divide 36 by 6 and then take away 3 to get the original number. This kind of activity makes children think of both the meaning of operations and the inter-connections between them.

Solving mathematical puzzles and contrived problems provides children with opportunities to use their numerical skills. This can be exemplified by the following problem-solving activity which involves counting, estimating, adding, and comparing numbers, just to mention a few.

> *Would you rather have your palm's worth of £1 coins or your height's worth of 5p coins?*

Realistic problems such as planning a 'value for money' holiday with £1500 using travel brochures or planning to set up a school shop are more open-ended, unlike the structured mathematical problems which have set solutions. The data for realistic problems are likely to be 'untidy and awkward'; this encourages children to select effective strategies and make adjustments. This kind of problem-solving helps children to make sensible interpretations of results. Realising, for example, there can be no 'remainder people' or 'half people' and that it is impossible to buy 'fractions of stamps'. Realistic problems are also likely to develop more rational thinking and ways of making sense of operations, and of course more perseverance, which is all important.

Solving mathematics puzzles which involve working with numbers helps children to develop a feel for numbers, which in turn helps them to acquire more confidence and flexibility to work with numbers.

The following examples of 'Arithmogons' (the number in the square must be the total of the numbers on either side) and 'Cryptarithms' are useful starting points to train children to become good problem solvers.

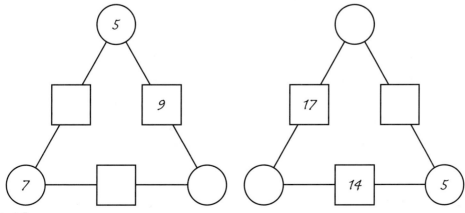

Arithmogons

Cryptarithms

1 Find A, B, C and D if

    ABC
+ ACB
    ——
    DDD and A, B, C, D are different digits.

2 Find A, B, C, D and E if

    ABC
+ CBA
    ——
    DED and A, B, C, D and E are different digits.

Solutions:

1 $A = 3, B = 2, C 5 = 4, D = 6.$

2 $A = 5, B = 4, C = 2, D 5 = 7, E = 8.$

Children can be trained to be more effective problem solvers. I have been involved in projects which have shown that many children who initially gave up solving problems, before they even studied the problem, becoming competent problem solvers after they have been told to follow some of the following strategies:

◆ Study the problem carefully. Read it a second time if necessary.

◆ What is it asking you to do?

◆ List what you know.

◆ Make a model or draw a picture to help you.

◆ What might the answer be like?

◆ Think about any similar problem you may have come across before.

◆ Work with other people to talk things through with someone.

Summary

This chapter dealt with aspects of teaching number. It started with a list of objectives provided by HMI (1985) for teaching and learning mathematics. Based on this list and the recommendations for teaching number in the *Framework for teaching mathematics*, ways of developing children's number sense were explored.

Chapter 3

Teaching mental mathematics

▬ ▬

Chapter 2 focused on aspects of teaching number, which included the teaching of the number system, number calculations and the use of number in solving problems. This chapter deals with a special aspect of number – the development of mental mathematics. Many teachers feel that this aspect of teaching mathematics will be greatly enhanced by the introduction of the National Numeracy Project and early indications are that the emphasis placed on mental mathematics has had a positive impact already. The interim evaluation of the numeracy project (Ofsted, 1998) acknowledged the improvement in the teaching of mental arithmetic in the pilot 'project schools'. This is very welcome news. However, it also needs to be stressed that the teaching of mental mathematics seems to be an aspect for which many teachers feel they need much support.

This chapter provides an overview of what is involved in teaching **mental mathematics** (all aspects of teaching number, not just calculations) and discusses, briefly, some feelings expressed by adults about their perceptions of mental mathematics. A list of strategies for undertaking mental calculations, which could usefully be taught to children, is included. Exemplifying materials, classroom examples and many practical suggestions are also provided. Although much of the content of this chapter deals with mental calculations, other aspects – such as an understanding of the place value system, the development of estimation skills and organisational issues – are also included.

What is mental mathematics?

A simple definition of mental mathematics is 'mathematics done in the head'. In the context of mental calculations, which this chapter mainly focuses on, it means calculating without the support of fingers, pencil and paper, counters or any physical equipment. One may, of course, use any or all of these physical aids in one's mind, as you will see when you read this chapter. An example of this was provided by six year-old Natalie who explained to her teacher how she used her fingers 'in her head' to do mental addition:

Teacher: *Natalie, can you add 8 and 5.*

Natalie: *(Moves her head to show that she was counting two imaginary objects saying, nine,* ten. (*Then starts counting three more imaginary objects*) 11, 12, 13. (*responds*), 13.

Teacher: Can you explain to me what you were doing? I saw you moving your head. What were you doing?

Natalie: I said eight. Then I counted two more fingers and got ten and then counted on three more and got 13.

Teacher: I didn't see you using your fingers. How did you use them.

Natalie: I used five 'pretend' fingers in my head.

To write or not to write

A question often raised in the context of mental calculations is: if you use pencil and paper to carry out calculations, do they stop being 'mental' calculations? My own belief is that jotting down ideas on paper is often necessary for extending one's ideas and for undertaking more complex mental calculations. The National Numeracy Project explains that children need to make 'informal' jottings when they calculate larger numbers 'when it will be hard for them to hold all the intermediate steps in their heads and so informal pencil and paper notes, recording some or all of their solution, become part of a mental strategy'. It goes on to say that these 'personal jottings may not be easy for someone else to follow, but they are a staging post to getting the right answer and acquiring fluency in mental calculation'.

What is oral mathematics?

Oral mathematics involves 'verbalising' your mathematical thinking. Being able to discuss mathematics enhances mental mathematics; in fact, I think mental and oral mathematics support each other.

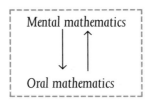

As is endorsed by the National Numeracy Project, effective teaching of mental mathematics will involve oral work. Explaining how mental calculations are carried out should help pupils to understand underlying mathematical concepts; it should also help them identify gaps in their knowledge. Listening to someone else's methods should encourage children to consider the relative efficiency of their own methods and make adjustments and refinements when necessary.

Is mental mathematics new?

The importance of children developing their mental mathematics skills has always been recognised. The Cockcroft Report (1982) devotes a whole section (paragraphs 314–320) to the teaching of 'mental mathematics'.

The report makes the following observations:

◆ Mental calculations play an important part in children being successful in mathematics;

◆ In many classrooms mental maths now occupies 'a far less prominent position in mathematics teaching . . .' and in some classrooms 'not practised at all';

◆ The trend of not focusing on mental maths should be reversed.

The report also suggests possible reasons for the lack of mental arithmetic lessons. Among these are the use of individualised mathematics programmes and worksheets which make it more difficult for a teacher to provide focused mental maths teaching. The other reason suggested is the wide range of ability of children in the class, making it difficult to find suitable questions for all children.

Other official documents, for example HMI (1985), have also stressed the importance of children learning and remembering number facts, terminology and number bonds. HMI also asserts that 'the quality of pupils' mathematical thinking is considerably enhanced by discussion'.

The National Curriculum (DES, 1991) has many references to mental arithmetic teaching. It requires teachers to give pupils opportunities to:

◆ develop flexible methods of working with number, orally and mentally;

◆ record in a variety of ways, including ways that relate to their mental work;

◆ develop a range of mental methods for finding, from known facts, those that they cannot recall.

As we know, the most recent development in mathematics education, the National Numeracy Strategy, recommends that structured teaching of mental mathematics be incorporated into the daily mathematics lesson. In the introductory part of the daily lesson teachers are expected to teach 'oral and mental calculations'. It is suggested that in this part of the lesson children are encouraged to participate in activities such as 'counting in steps' and 'playing games' which encourage rapid recall of number facts. Children should also be taught how to figure out new facts from learnt facts which have been committed to memory.

There is no doubt that in the context of implementing the National Numeracy Strategy, the teaching of mental arithmetic will receive a high profile. How do we provide our children with high quality learning experiences?

Teaching mental mathematics

Making a start

When considering how to teach mental mathematics to children, both emotional and cognitive aspects of learning need to be considered. So to start with, take a few minutes to reflect on your own school experiences in mental mathematics. Before reading on, write down a few words or phrases which come to mind which describe your feelings and thoughts.

The following comments were provided by one of the teachers attending our in-service sessions:

Do these words capture some of your feelings?

It is likely that these strong feelings are still with many of us. Failing to complete mental arithmetic tests for all sorts of reasons – lack of speed or concentration, lack of understanding of concepts or not possessing sound strategies – was common is my schooldays; perhaps many of the readers have experienced these too. So here is a challenge for us all; how can we teach mental mathematics to children effectively and at the same time make the lessons meaningful and enjoyable?

Helping children to develop competence in mental maths

It is reasonable to assume that children need to develop two types of competencies for mental calculations:

◆ instant recall of facts;

◆ 'figuring out' facts from known facts.

Based on research evidence, Askew *et al* (1997a) suggest that these two aspects of mental mathematics, which they refer to as 'known facts' and 'derived facts' are complementary. The authors provide the example of a Key Stage 1 pupil who knew the fact '5 + 5 = 10' and used that fact to figure out 5 + 6 = 11 as one more than 5 + 5. A Key Stage 2 pupil figuring out 40 × 24 = 960 from 'knowing' 4 × 25 = 100 is another example.

Askew *et al*'s model in Figure 3.1 is a useful guide for planning to teach mental mathematics.

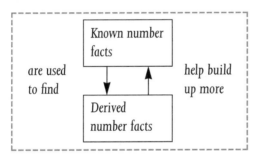

Figure 3.1 Planning guide for teaching mental mathematics

What do we mean by 'known' facts and 'derived' facts? What strategies do we use for mental calculations? A practical task should demonstrate this:

Calculate the following (questions shown in A's list) in your head. If you are doing this with a

A's list	B's list
8 × 7	7 + 6
32 + 226 + 28	350 − 126
210 ÷ 50	33 − 2.5
29 times 13	39 times 19
800 + 600	How many 19p stamps can you buy for £5.00
25% of £3600 is =	23 × 400 =

colleague or friend, then use the questions in both lists — A and B being partners — and take it in turns to ask each other (A asking B and B asking A).

The purpose of this exercise is to find out what strategies you and your partner use for doing mental calculations. Try to relax, and tell your partner how you performed each of the calculations giving her time to record your strategies. If your partner needs more information, she may gently probe you further.

After all the calculation are carried out, look at the list of strategies which have been used and try to analyse them. It is likely that your strategies are similar to those listed below.

Strategies for mental arithmetic

◆ Recall of fact, 'just know' it. 8×7 and $7 + 6$ are likely to be in this category. But it is also common for people to work out 7×7 and add 7 more to find the answer to 8×7 or $6 + 6 + 1$ to find the answer to $7 + 6$.

◆ Re-arranging the sum to make it more manageable;
$32 + 226 + 28 = 32 + 28 + 226 = 60 + 226 = 286.$

◆ Use a fact from memory and adjust for current use; There are 2 fifties in 100 so there are 4 fifties in 210.

◆ Use a number line strategy; to calculate $350 - 126$, count on from 126 to $200 = 74$ then to 300 and then add 50.

◆ Use the mental imagery of previous experiences: sums, fraction cake, number line to calculate $33 - 2.5$.

◆ Estimate a 'possible' answer. You work out: you can buy 5 twenty (rounding 19p) pence stamps for £1, so for £5.00 you can buy 25 stamps, instead of attempting to perform a long division in your head!

◆ Knowing a collection of facts which one can use; 25% means a quarter: so 25% of £3600 is £900.

◆ Use 10s and 100s as multiples.
$23 \times 400 = 23 \times 4 \times 100 = 92 \times 100 = 9200.$

It is useful to remember that children do not automatically adopt the above strategies; focused teaching does help them to acquire proficiency in mental calculations.

What should children learn?

Based on the Programme of Study for mathematics in the National Curriculum and the content of the National Numeracy Framework, it is possible to draw up a list of what should be taught to children.

It is reasonable to expect children to commit the following to memory. At Key Stage 1 they should remember facts such as:

◆ addition and subtraction facts to 20;

◆ doubles of numbers up to 20;

◆ instant recall of pairs of numbers which add up to 10;

◆ multiplication and division facts relating to twos, fives, tens.

At Key Stage 2 pupils can be expected to:

◆ build on their previous knowledge of addition and subtraction facts to 20;

◆ learn multiplication and division facts for all pairs of numbers up to 10×10;

◆ know pairs of numbers which add up to 100; for example $35 + 65 = 100$;

◆ totals of decimal numbers; $0.3 + 0.7 = 1$ and so on.

As well as knowing and being able to recall number facts at Key Stage 1, children should be able to calculate using the following strategies:

◆ add numbers in any order knowing that, in the operation for addition, the order of numbers does not make a difference to the total;

◆ use learnt facts to figure out new facts; for example use the known fact that $20 + 20 = 40$ to figure out $20 + 21 = 41$;

◆ find near doubles and use double facts to work out the answer; $35 + 36 = 35 + 35 + 1 = 70 + 1 = 71$.

At Key Stage 2 children can be expected to:

◆ use known number facts to figure out other facts;

◆ learn about properties of number; multiples, factors and squares, primes, cubes and square roots.

At both Key Stages children should:

◆ learn that subtraction is the inverse of addition;

◆ understand multiplication as repeated addition, and division both as sharing and repeated subtraction;

◆ develop mental methods of computation with whole numbers up to 100;

◆ develop a range of non-calculator methods of computation that involve addition and subtraction of whole numbers, multiplication and division of up to three-digits by two-digit whole numbers.

How do we develop children's mental mathematics?

This section focuses on how teachers can support children to develop their mental and oral mathematics skills. Before I start discussing strategies, I need to emphasise that, in this section, I will include both 'mental calculations' and other aspects of 'doing mathematics in the head', such as developing mental imagery, estimating and so on. Hence the phrase 'mental mathematics' is used rather than restricting the discussion to aspects of calculations only.

Effective teaching of mental mathematics should include the following strands:

◆ understanding of number concepts and properties of number;

◆ efficient mental calculations;

◆ quick recall of facts;

◆ strategies to use and apply number.

Although the above list provides a useful framework to start considering ways of teaching mental mathematics, it is not intended that the four components be taught separately. 'Good' mental mathematics activities will often address more than one of the components as can be seen in the next section.

Making it happen

In this section, examples of a range of practical strategies used by teachers are given. These are provided in the form of ideas. The focus, however, is not on the ideas themselves, but on the way they are used to develop mental mathematics. The sub-headings used are arbitrary because one activity may address more than one concept; but they do try to highlight the main objectives of each section as well as the chosen activities. Readers who are interested in exploring aspects of teaching mental mathematics and ideas in more detail, are advised to refer to a series of mental mathematics books for teachers (Koshy, 1998).

Developing mental imagery

During the mental maths session, ask the children to visualise:

Close your eyes and try to see number 5. Then open your eyes and tell me what you see. Discuss with the group what they saw, number five on the dice, fingers, the number 5 as a numeral?

Try to see 10, 12, and so on.

What do you see when I say half? It is likely that all the images 'seen' by the children will 'express' the concept of one whole one cut into two equal parts. An apple cut into two equal halves? A piece of squared paper divided into 2 parts. Focus the discussion on what half really means. Does it always mean one whole divided into two? *What do you see when I say half of 12? What do you see now?* During these discussions a teacher can gather much information about children's level of conceptual understanding as well as of the existence of any misconceptions.

Caroline, a Year 5 teacher, who used visual imagery of cakes to teach decimals by providing children with card collections of whole cakes, tenths of cakes and hundredths of cakes to model decimal numbers, claimed that her children's facility to order decimal numbers in their written exercises doubled as a result of this activity. Children had developed strong visual imagery of the sizes of decimal numbers. One pupil explained her strategy for placing numbers 1.23, 12.3, 0.123, 12.03 and 21.3 in order, starting with the smallest:

Teacher: *Melanie, can you explain how you ordered these numbers?*

Melanie: *You see miss, I imagined the cakes we used from the tray and thought; well, there is no whole cake at all in this number nought point one two three, that has to be the smallest. (With a chuckle) I suppose that is hardly worth having when you could have a portion of 21 whole cakes and three tenths of a cake. I imagined them all as pieces of cake. That is how I did it.*

Melanie's teacher commented on the difficulty experienced by children in dealing with decimals numbers, a fact borne out by research. Building up mental imagery may be one way of tackling this difficulty. For her decimal teaching programme, Caroline used other visual aids too, such as squared paper models of decimals, metre sticks, measuring pots and so on. Here I need to stress the importance of discussion. When working with practical materials we must not assume that the apparatus will do the teaching; it is the teacher who teaches by letting children discuss with the teacher and the class what they are doing with the apparatus. Practical materials can help with the internalisation of concepts, as we can see from the above example, but it seems that Caroline's whole-class discussion of decimal cakes made a substantial impact. Text books are full of pictures modelling decimals and fractions but their use alone is not enough.

'Missing number' ideas

It is useful for children to visualise number bonds, number lines and number squares. The following whole-class activities provide useful opportunities for teachers to help to move children from what is practical to the 'abstract'.

'Hide the beans'

Place some coloured beans, say 10 in total, on an overhead projector or on the floor where all the children can see them. Let the children count and make sure how many there are; then the teacher hides some of them under a plastic cup. Children can only see how many are outside and are asked to work out how many are hidden under the cup. Change the numbers hidden under the cup a few times, encouraging the children to verbalise number facts modelled from the beans activity. If 7 are hidden from a total of 10, then the number fact 7 and 3 makes 10 is demonstrated through this activity. This activity can be repeated with threaded beads, cubes, pegboards and so on. In all cases it will be very interesting to ask children how they had worked out the missing number.

'The hungry caterpillar'

After reading the story of *The Hungry Caterpillar* and discussing its daily intake of food, you may make a sliding strip of food 'fed into the caterpillar' to learn about missing numbers.

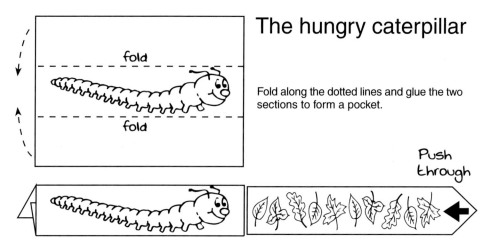

The hungry caterpillar

Fold along the dotted lines and glue the two sections to form a pocket.

Show the children the picture of the caterpillar and the leaves.
Ask them to count the leaves.

Slide the leaves into the pocket behind the caterpillar, but leave three leaves showing. Say to the children: 'How many leaves has the caterpillar eaten?'

Using the sliding model you can ask: how many leaves are there altogether?

Slide a few of the leaves into the pocket and ask: how many leaves can you see, can you work out how many have been eaten? This activity is a useful preparation for recording missing number sums such as:

$\square + 3 = 10$
$4 + \square = 10$

Activities such as the 'missing beans' and 'caterpillars' can be used several times with different combination of numbers for reinforcement of number bonds. Again, discussion is important.

'Missing spots'

Dice provide a multitude of opportunities for children to practise both the missing number concept and addition and subtraction bonds.

With the whole class watching, hold one die, and ask:

I have one die here. Who knows how a normal 1 to 6 die is numbered?

If no one knows the principle, then demonstrate that two opposite sides of a die always add up to 7. Hide one side and ask children to work out the number on the other side. Ask children to verbalise how they worked it out. Some interesting mental work should emerge.

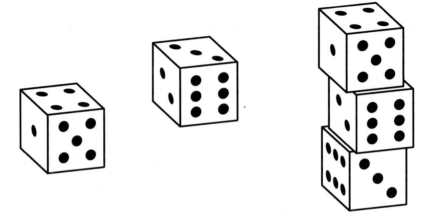

Using more dice you can ask:

Who can tell me how many spots there are, altogether, on one die? 2 dice? 3 dice?

I am going to place one die on top of the other, can you tell me what the hidden numbers are? What if I did this with three dice?

In how many different ways can you get number 6, or number 10, throwing two dice together?

'Number squares and number lines'

Visualising number patterns and number lines is another way of helping children to develop a 'feel' for number. As a whole class activity, using an OHT of a number square, you could ask the children to study how numbers are arranged on a number square and describe it to the class (let them look at a number square for a few minutes). Then cover one or two of the numbers and ask them to work out the 'missing' numbers. After practising this a few times, the whole class – individually or in pairs – could be given missing numbers of the number square to be filled in.

In the same way, number lines can be used to reinforce how whole numbers, negative numbers, fractions and decimals fit into the number system. These, of course, can be used at different levels. Here are some ideas:

◆ Use a number line marked from 1 to 100; hide some numbers and ask children to work out the missing numbers. In a whole class situation, children can be asked to use number cards and blu-tack to do this.

◆ Use a number line, showing only the first and the last of a series, for example, 300–400, and ask children to place cards with 330, 360, 390 and so on, in the right places.

◆ Using empty number lines, ask children to fill in parts of decimal or fraction number lines.

1	2	3	4	5	6	7	8	9	10
11	12	13	14	15	16	17	18	19	20
21	22	23	24	25	26	27	28	29	30
31	32	33	34	35	36	37	38	39	40
41	42	43	44	45	46	47	48	49	50
51	52	53	54	55	56	57	58	59	60
61	62	63	64	65	66	67	68	69	70
71	72	73	74	75	76	77	78	79	80
81	82	83	84	85	86	87	88	89	90
91	92	93	94	95	96	97	98	99	100

'Number squares and number lines'

Mental models of the number system

Our number system is based on the place values of digits. As I discussed in detail in Chapter 2, an appreciation that the position of the digit determines the value of the digit is an important factor in children developing confidence in working with number, estimating skills and efficient calculating strategies. During a mental maths lesson, it will be useful to introduce arrow cards, calculators, place value boards and so on and to discuss the 'numeracy' principles embedded in the activities. Chapter 2 and Chapter 5 provide many such activities which can be used with either small groups or a whole class.

Use of mathematical games

The use of mathematical games is recommended in the *Framework* as a way of developing an understanding of mathematical concepts. Most teachers are aware of the potential of mathematical learning from mathematical games and may have used them for many years. What may change now is the way we use mathematical games. For example, instead of small groups playing games, a game may be used as the basis of the introductory part of a lesson with clear objectives of what is being taught. A game such as such as 'get-four-in-a line' can be played as a team game. This will make possible, not only maximum interaction, but also opportunities for practising mental recall of number facts, estimation and number calculations. There is also the aspect of motivation associated with the concept of a game, which most practising teachers will know about. The game shown opposite, played by a class of Year 5 children, in two teams, for 10 minutes will illustrate the potential of using mathematics games for teaching mental mathematics.

The teacher, David, had made a list of what he expected children to be taught. After playing the game he asked the children to tell him what they had learnt from playing the game. Evidence of learning was provided by children's comments:

> I know 25 × 3 is 75 and 35 × 20 is 700.
>
> I realised that a number multiplied by 5 will end in a five or a zero. I learnt it when my mate Danny told me. I quickly saw it.
>
> I know three long multiplication facts I did not know before.

The teacher also reported that after having observed the interest and motivation in this lesson, he gave the children a copy of the game to take

Get four-in-a-line

Take it in turns.

Pick two numbers from the set and multiply them to get a number on the grid. If your answer is right (a referee, with a calculator will check it). Place a counter on the number in the grid. when you get four counters in-a-line, you get a point. Keep playing till most of the numbers on the grid are used up.

35   15   10   20

3   45   55   25

50   30   5

1050	90	300	165	75	1500
125	700	1250	525	875	550
60	1500	15	675	375	90
165	450	300	1250	1050	1125
875	550	525	150	600	700
75	105	15	675	135	375

home so that they could prepare for playing it the following week. The result was a more productive and dynamic session which provided more evidence of children having practised multiplication facts involving more challenging numbers.

Loop cards

For practising calculations and instant recall, one can use card-games such as 'loop cards'. Sets of 'loop cards' are excellent resources for helping children to develop alertness and speed in instant recall. An example of an effective and dynamic lesson using loop cards shown on the video 'Teachers Count' (Ofsted, 1998) has encouraged many teachers to design and use loop cards with their children. The idea of loop cards is not new; an excellent book *Loop Cards – Mathematics for Primary Schools* on the use of loop cards is provided by Pinel (1988).

The idea is based on what the name 'loop' suggests. Loop cards are sets of cards which form loops. They are designed in such a way that a card is followed by another which provides the solution to the previous one. For example, in a set of loop cards which is designed to practise number operations, a set of cards may look like this:

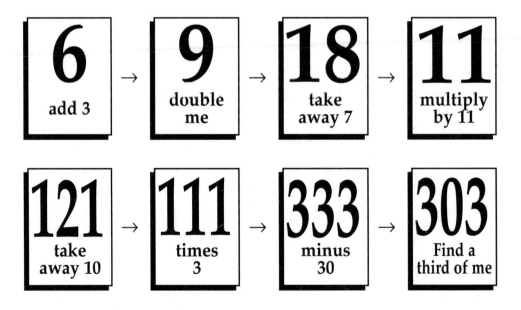

and so on.

These are 8 cards from a set. The first card has number 6 as its starter number and an operation – add 3. The next card in the loop will have 9 written on it and another operation 'double me', which will lead you to the third card in the loop which says 18 and asks you to do the operation 'take away 7'. The fourth card has the solution 11 and multiply by 11 and so on. The cards are designed in such a way that the last card completes the loop.

You can have as few or as many cards as you like, depending on the size of the groups using the game. The following suggestions may help to make the most effective use of loop cards.

◆ A loop game can be played by a whole class – say 32 children – sitting in a circle. Until children get used to the game, it may be better to have *exactly* 32 cards in the loop. One child calls out a card 'I have 6, add 3'. The pupil with the card 9 written on it will call out 'I have 9, double me' which will alert the child with 18 written on his or her card to say 'I have 18 take away 7 . . .' and so on, until all 32 children have participated in the game.

◆ The loop game can also be played by small groups.

◆ As children get used to the cards, one child can have more than one card.

◆ It is possible to get two children to share a card for paired work.

◆ A set of cards can be used to target a specific operation (multiplication) or for practising mixed operations. The descriptions on the cards will depend on the objectives. Some examples of using cards are to practise:
  – one operation – addition
  – all four rules of number
  – operation on fractions, decimals, percentages
  – measures, length, weight, time and so on
  – equivalence of fractions and decimals
  – relationships between percentages, fractions and decimals

◆ Loop cards can be used with all age groups. For younger children these can be used to practise mathematical words such as '2 more' and '4 less' or to introduce a variety of words and symbols to describe a concept. For example, they could be used to reinforce the idea that 'three more' and 'add 3' and '+3' do the same thing to a number.

In my experience, the usefulness of loop cards is indisputable; they help children to rehearse number facts and skills in a motivating, group context and to develop accuracy, speed and recall of calculations. Loop cards also offer teachers an effective way of practising the inter-connections between concepts. However, one needs to use the cards sensitively with children and be aware of those children who may not have the necessary speed to join in a whole-class loop card activity. Pairing children to share a card often helps.

It is also useful to bear in mind that loop cards are equally effective in smaller groups.

Children often enjoy making sets of loop cards. Creating loop cards is a challenging activity; it involves them in useful mathematical processes such as analysing concepts, organising ideas and checking solutions.

Using a calculator

Developing a feel for number is an essential part of teaching mental mathematics. This involves children understanding the structure and composition of numbers and being able to analyse the principles involved. In this context, a calculator can be of much use. Many activities such as 'broken calculator', 'six discrimination' and 'place invaders', provided in Chapter 5, encourage children to analyse the structure of numbers, make sense of number operations, estimate and calculate mentally.

Word games

Both mathematical reasoning and oral communication can be generated by providing mathematical activities such as 'What is my secret number?' The following example from a Year 3 class demonstrates the potential of this activity where the teacher gave the following clues to the whole class and asked them to guess her secret number.

My secret number is:

◆ between 1 and 100

◆ It is bigger than 50

◆ It is a square number

◆ It is a multiple of 4

◆ It is nearer to 70 than it is to 100

What is my number?

Children were asked to spend 2 minutes, in groups of three, to work out the secret number and to prove to themselves that they were right before sharing it with the whole class. After working out a few secret numbers, it was the children's turn to select and work out some clues to make up their own secret numbers, in pairs, and share them with the whole class.

Using dartboards

Using different versions of dartboards provides another opportunity for children to be engaged in mental calculations, pose their own questions and estimate solutions.

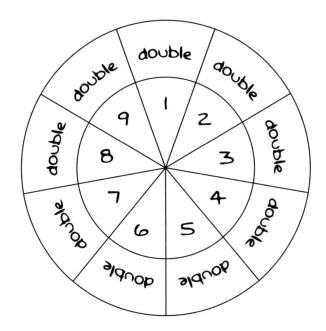

During an introductory lesson with a Year 2 class, the teacher asked her children the following questions, based on the displayed enlarged version of the darts activity:

Using three counters as darts what is the highest number you can make? How did you do it? How did you add the numbers? What number did you put first?

What is the lowest number you can get?

Can you make exactly 11?

You can also ask children to pose their own questions.

Function machines

For developing efficient strategies for mental calculations, the use of function machines is strongly encouraged. You could have a box or grid marked 'in' and 'out' and get children to feed in numbers with either you or the children selecting the operation.

An effective way of using a function machine is to hide someone under a table with a cloth over it, to act as calculating machine performing the function. This will need preparation to make sure that the 'hidden human

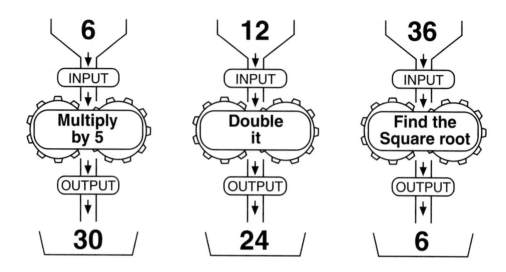

machine' under the table provides correct answers to questions, unless you occasionally want to test children's alertness and reaction with a deliberate mistake made by the machine.

Estimating activities

A 'Likely or unlikely' activity was used for a whole class discussion in a Year 4 class. Alison, the teacher, selected this activity in order to:

> . . . make children think about ideas about measurement. Quite often children calculate measures mechanically without any real understanding. They have no strategies for checking the answers, for estimating or considering whether an answer makes sense. Making them think about the ideas and justify their solutions to others was a very useful process.

Alison asked the children to consider the following statements and say whether they are likely or unlikely and give reasons for their choice:

> Your hair grows 5 centimetres a day
>
> Your weight is about 2 kilograms
>
> Your teacher's height is 165 centimetres
>
> A person can walk 70 kilometres in an hour
>
> A glass of lemonade is about 30 ml

Generating facts from known facts

Asking children to look at facts they know and generate new facts from them is also a worthwhile activity. When children were asked to write down all the facts they can derive from a given statement the following response was offered by a child:

Derived Facts.

$$0.7 \times 8 = 5.6$$

$$80 \times 7 = 560 \qquad 8 \times 8 = 64 \qquad 800 \times 700 = 560000$$

$$56 \div 8 = 7 \quad\boxed{7 \times 8 = 56}\quad 56 \div 7 = 8$$

$$0.7 \times 0.8 = 0.56$$

$$80 \times 70 = 5,600 \qquad 7 \times 7 = 49 \qquad 8 \times 70 = 560$$

$$0.8 \times 7 = 5.6$$

As mentioned previously, the purpose of including various activities was to enable the reader to think about effective ways of conducting mental mathematics lessons. Many of the activities included in other chapters of this book can be adapted for use in mental mathematics lessons.

Organisation issues

Some organisational models have already been incorporated into previous sections of this chapter when examples of activities were presented. A real challenge for teachers is how to organise mental mathematics sessions in such a way that all pupils will achieve maximum benefit. A question often raised is 'how can I teach mental mathematics to a whole class of children with different abilities, learning styles and speeds?' The question is a very reasonable one. I think the following suggestions may be useful:

◆ Provide children with a variety of models of doing mathematics in the head. It may be that you will use some of your lessons for 'quick-fire' type of questions which encourage speed and recall. The questions may be selected from the topic currently being learnt or designed to practise addition bonds or multiplication bonds. Many of the commercially produced materials provide exercises designed to achieve this objective. If the only mental mathematics children experience is based on teaching recall, they will be deprived of opportunities to develop an understanding of the principles behind number calculations, estimating skills and developing a sense of number.

◆ Vary the style of the lesson. It may that within the structure of the whole class lesson, children can be asked to work in pairs or small groups to discuss the best strategy they can think of for carrying out a calculation – say 350 divided by 29 – before sharing their ideas with the rest of the class. Children can be asked to work in pairs, asking questions in turn, and finding out how their partners had worked out the sums, in a similar style to that discussed earlier in this chapter.

◆ Team games provide another way of organising your mental maths session. The added advantage of these is the level of motivation they provide, which is important in encouraging positive attitudes towards mental calculations.

Teachers on our in-service courses have often acknowledged how good planning and thinking contribute to the effectiveness of their lessons. The following issues may be of particular importance.

Differentiation in mental maths lessons

Children learn mathematics and recall facts at different speeds. This poses a particular challenge in mental mathematics lessons. If your school sets children, that should help to reduce the range of abilities in the same class. If you are teaching a mixed ability class, how can you make sure that all children are kept suitably challenged and everyone's contributions are valued? The final chapter in this book deals with issues of differentiation. The following strategies have been found useful by teachers in the context of teaching mental mathematics:

◆ Use targeted questions. In a whole-class mental maths lesson, two kinds of children may feel frustrated; the 'fast' workers who will have their hands up all the time and may not be asked any questions at all and those who cannot either recall or figure out the answers fast enough to make a contribution. This has implications for the type of questions you provide. If all the questions are always pitched at the 'average' level, there will be insufficient challenge for able pupils. Targeting questions carefully at individuals according to their ability to respond is one way of providing the challenge. This aspect is discussed, using examples, in Chapter 6.

◆ Within a whole-class teaching situation, let children work in pairs or small groups on differentiated tasks. This provides you with an opportunity to match the task to the level of ability of the child.

◆ In some lessons discourage children from putting their hands up. Ask them to put their answers in their heads and wait to be asked.

◆ For the 'quick-fire' type of questions, let children use number cards to show their answers when the teacher invites the whole class to do so. This enables the teacher to study all the responses quickly and make mental notes of those children who may have problems.

◆ Answers can sometimes be recorded on a sheet of paper so that the teacher can select individual children to respond.

◆ Use open-ended questions in order to facilitate children to work at their level of ability.

Issues of grouping

Many schools are now setting children for mathematics lessons, according to their ability. Whether 'set' into groups or divided into ability groups within the class, the following points may be useful to consider:

◆ The importance of listening to each other should be insisted on. When children verbalise their thoughts and methods, the benefits can only be derived if the others listen to them. In many classrooms training in listening skills would be a worthwhile exercise.

◆ To make your mental mathematics lessons active and interactive, it is advisable to get all children to participate. The teacher needs to consider different roles for children to participate according to the task in hand: for demonstration, being a referee or score keeper.

◆ It is useful, within the introductory session, to set tasks for small groups to discuss ideas and report back to the whole class. This type of group work is useful when children are engaged in sorting out word problems or puzzles which involve reasoning, hypothesising, checking and proving.

◆ You could encourage small groups of children, in turn, to put up interactive displays of number facts, number stories, number statements and so on prior to the class discussion on a mathematical topic.

A high profile for mental mathematics

It is likely that in all classrooms teachers will introduce regular, structured mental mathematics lessons as part of the National Numeracy Strategy. It is also likely that this is an area which may be 'new' to many teachers. As was stressed earlier in this chapter, in order to achieve effective teaching of mental mathematics, the teacher needs to address two aspects: the content to be taught and the style in which it is taught. Creating the right environment for learning mental mathematics will undoubtedly be part of the strategies adopted. The following ideas have been found useful by practising teachers:

◆ Let children have mental mathematics kits, perhaps in zipped bags. Part of this kit could be provided by the teacher; but some of the items could be made by the children. A 'good' number kit may contain sets of 0–9 digit cards, marked and blank number-lines, dice and a favourite number-game which fits in with the weekly class objectives.

◆ Encourage children to keep a 'Facts' book in which they can keep a record of new facts they have learnt. Mathematical words, symbols and signs may be recorded in the book. The teacher may have a set time for making entries in the book or it could be part of homework.

◆ Have interactive displays in the classroom or in the corridor. Children could be invited to put up their responses to questions: *Which number between 0 and 100 has the most number of factors?* or *The answer is 10, what are the questions?* Let the displays stay for at least a whole week before you discuss the responses; this will ensure that children are studying, analysing, wondering and reflecting on the responses.

◆ Focus on one or two mathematical facts each week. Design posters illustrating these facts which will enable children to internalise the ideas behind these facts.

◆ Make mental mathematics lessons enjoyable by including mathematics games and 'close your eyes' kind of activities, instead of just using 'question and answer' sessions every day of the week.

◆ Be wary of using commercially produced materials requiring 'ten sums a day' during all mental maths sessions. These are useful for checking purposes, but little will be achieved by children working through closed sums on a page as their only experiences of developing mental strategies.

Discussion in mental mathematics

Effective teaching of mental mathematics will involve children verbalising their methods and mental strategies in both whole-class and small group situations. Listening to others will help children to consider their methods and their relative efficiency; this should lead to a refinement of strategies. Of course, we also all learn from listening to other people's explanations.

Discussions during mental mathematics lessons can take many forms and styles. Some of these are listed below:

◆ With the whole class listening, the teacher asks questions; these questions may be closed, such as: Add 38 and 59, what is the answer?; or open-ended: when I added two numbers the answer was 30, what were my two numbers? In both cases, children can be asked to explain how they arrived at the answer. By asking probing questions children can be encouraged to verbalise their thought processes, providing insights to both the teacher and other pupils. Here it may be pertinent to add that the nature and usefulness of the responses will depend on the quality and the types of questions asked by the teacher. During these discussions, the teacher may direct specific questions in order to highlight the relative advantages of certain methods or to expose sensitively how and why some 'child methods' may not be efficient.

◆ Children may be to asked to work in pairs, taking it in turns to ask questions and ask for explanations. After the paired work they can be invited to explain their partner's methods to the whole class. This responsibility of having to report back often makes children take the paired task and probing more seriously.

◆ Children can be asked to work in small groups within the structure of a whole-class lesson and to investigate number ideas which involve mental calculations, to solve number problems or puzzles mentally; reporting back can be optional.

Assessing mathematical learning from mental maths sessions

Your mental mathematics sessions can provide some of the most useful insights into children's understanding of mathematical concepts, provided these lessons include probing questions from the teacher and children responding orally to probing questions. In order to make effective assessments of children's conceptual understanding, the following strategies may be useful:

During your mathematics lessons

◆ Use direct questions to assess children's knowledge of number facts.

◆ Include regular times for children to verbalise their strategies. Ask children: tell me how you did that? That sounds very interesting, tell me more. Can someone else tell us what Diane has just explained? How would you do it?

◆ Give children some short 'multiple choice' type of questions or 'true or false' questions to do and ask them to explain the reasons for their choice.

◆ It is often useful to ask children to look at work done on OHTs or on the board by 'imaginary' children, to ascertain if the answers are correct and then analyse any mistakes and misconceptions.

Summary

This chapter focused on what we mean by mental mathematics and what the expectations have been over the last few decades. The readers were invited to join a practical task in order to highlight some useful strategies for teaching mental arithmetic. A list of what may be expected from children was provided and practical ideas were offered to support the teacher to change the expectations into reality. Issues relating to classroom organisation were also considered.

It is hoped that this chapter has provided the reader with a structure to look at aspects of teaching mental mathematics. Many teachers and teacher trainees have found the ideas in this chapter very useful and have acknowledged that the quality of their lessons has improved a great deal. Hopefully, you too will reflect on the ideas discussed in this chapter. Perhaps you could write down those things that have made an impact on you after reading this chapter.

Chapter 4

Planning, teaching and assessing numeracy

Good planning, effective teaching and assessing are the three inter-related aspects which contribute to raising children's achievement.

The planning, teaching and assessing cycle in Figure 4.1 (Mitchell and Koshy, 1995), shows how the three elements are related. Think for a moment about how these elements fit into your current classroom practice. The mathematics *Framework* provides some guidance on all three aspects. The aim of this chapter is to explore these aspects in more depth and stimulate some reflection on the issues. The contents of this chapter are organised into three sections. First, issues relating to planning are addressed, then it focuses on the structure of the *daily mathematics lesson* and the recommended teaching style; some sample lesson plans are provided for you to consider different features of the daily lesson. The final section deals with the assessment of children's learning.

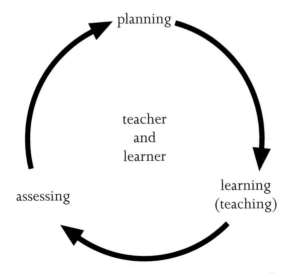

Figure 4.1 The planning, teaching and assessing cycle

Planning

Take a minute to think about the features that make a good teaching plan. A short list of those features may look like:

◆ clear objectives which also provide a structure for the assessment of learning;

- guidance of what should be taught to children;

- differentiation, so that children will be able to manage the work as well as be suitably challenged;

- progression of ideas.

Guidance for planning

As you unpack the *Framework*, you will see that it provides you with a list of key objectives and explanations of what to teach children. It also contains elements of progression. Although it may take a little time to become familiar with the planning grids and examples in the *Framework*, it is time well spent as it will help to bring greater consistency of content and expectations both within your school and between your school and other schools in the country. Many teachers find the **supplementary examples** section very useful, especially those who are anxious about their subject knowledge. As for the mathematics co-ordinators, they feel relieved that each school does not have to produce its own list of objectives, as the *Framework* provides the basis of a scheme of work.

First, let us take a look at the planning section of the *Framework*. As we have been accustomed over the past few years, it deals with three levels of planning:

- **long-term plans**: what to teach over the whole **year**, referred to as the *teaching programme*;

- **medium-term plans**: these contain a list of objectives you would be teaching each **term** and guidance on when to teach them; planning grids are provided for this. They are optional, but it makes sense to use them;

- **short-term plans**: these are plans for a **week** or **fortnight**, listing activities, key questions and organisational strategies. The school may design its own short-term planning system or you may consider adopting the model presented later in this chapter.

From the short-term plan, **daily mathematics lessons** are planned. This will be dealt with later.

Long-term plan

The yearly plan is set out with the key objectives in bold.

Teaching programme: Year 1

Numbers and the number system

2–7   **Counting, properties of
numbers and number sequences**

2   ◆ Know the number names and
recite them in order to at least
20, from and back to zero.

2   ◆ **Count reliably at least 20
objects.**

2, 4, 6   ◆ Describe and extend number
sequences:
**count on and back in ones
from any small number,
and in tens from and back
to zero;**
count on in twos from zero,
then one, and begin to
recognise odd or even
numbers to about 20 as 'every
other number';
count in steps of 5 from zero
to 20 or more, then back
again;
begin to count on in steps of 3
from zero.

8–15   **Place value and ordering**

8   ◆ **Read and write numerals
from 0 to at least 20.**

8   ◆ Begin to know what each digit
in a two-digit number
represents. Partition a 'teens'
number and begin to partition
larger two-digit numbers into
a multiple of 10 and ones
(TU).

10   ◆ **Understand and use the
vocabulary of comparing
and ordering numbers,**
including ordinal numbers to
at least 20. Use the = sign to
represent equality.
Compare two familiar
numbers, say which is more
or less, and give a number
which lies between them.

12   ◆ **Within the range 0 to 30,
say the number that is 1 or
10 more or less than any
given number.**

14   ◆ **Order numbers to at least
20,** and position them on a
number track.

16–19   **Estimating**

16   ◆ Understand and use the
vocabulary of estimation.
Give a sensible estimate of a
number of objects that can be
checked by counting (e.g. up
to about 30 objects).

Calculations

24–29   **Understanding addition and
subtraction**

24, 28   ◆ **Understand the operation
of addition, and of
subtraction (as 'take away',
'difference',** and 'how many
more to make'), **and use the
related vocabulary.**
Begin to recognise that
addition can be done in any
order.
Begin to use the +, − and =
signs to record mental
calculations in a number
sentence, and to recognise the
use of symbols such as □ and
△ to stand for an unknown
number.

26   ◆ Begin to recognise that more
than two numbers can be
added together.

**Figure 4.2 The Yearly Teaching Programme for Year 1, from the
Framework for teaching mathematics**

30–31 Rapid recall of addition and subtraction facts

30 ◆ **Know by heart:**
all pairs of numbers with a total of 10 (e.g. 3 + 7);
addition facts for all pairs of numbers with a total up to at least 5, and the corresponding subtraction facts;
addition doubles of all numbers to at least 5 (e.g. 4 + 4).
Begin to know:
addition facts for all pairs of numbers with a total up to at least 10, and the corresponding subtraction facts.

32–41 Mental calculation strategies (+ and −)

32 ◆ Use knowledge that addition can be done in any order to do mental calculations more efficiently. For example:
put the larger number first and count on in ones, including beyond 10 (e.g. 7 + 5);
begin to partition into '5 and a bit' when adding 6, 7, 8 or 9, then recombine (e.g. $6 + 8 = 5 + 1 + 5 + 3 = 10 + 4 = 14$).

32 ◆ Identify near doubles, using doubles already known (e.g. 6 + 5).

34 ◆ Add 9 to single-digit numbers by adding 10 then subtracting 1.

34 ◆ Use patterns of similar calculations(e.g. $10 − 0 = 10$, $10 − 1 = 9$, $10 − 2 = 8 \ldots$).

36, 38 ◆ Use known number facts and place value to add or subtract a pair of numbers mentally within the range 0 to at least 10, then 0 to at least 20.

40 ◆ Begin to bridge through 10, and later 20, when adding a single-digit number.

Solving problems

60–61 Making decisions

60 ◆ Choose and use appropriate number operations and mental strategies to solve problems.

62–65 Reasoning about numbers or shapes

62 ◆ Solve simple mathematical problems or puzzles; recognise and predict from simple patterns and relationships. Suggest extensions by asking 'What if . . .?' or 'What could I try next?'

64 ◆ Investigate a general statement about familiar numbers or shapes by finding examples that satisfy it.

64 ◆ Explain methods and reasoning orally.

66–71 Problems involving 'real life', money or measures

66, 68, ◆ **Use mental strategies to**
solve simple problems set
in 'real life', money
70 or measurement contexts,
using counting, addition,
subtraction, doubling and
halving, explaining
methods and reasoning
orally.

68 ◆ Recognise coins of different values.
Find totals and change from up to 20p.
Work out how to pay an exact sum using smaller coins.

90–93 Organising and using data

90, 92 ◆ Solve a given problem by sorting, classifying and organising information in simple ways, such as:
using objects or pictures;
in a list or simple table.
Discuss and explain results.

Figure 4.2 contd

Measures, shape and space

72–79 Measures

72 ◆ Understand and use the vocabulary related to length, mass and capacity. **Compare two lengths, masses or capacities by direct comparison**; extend to more than two. Measure using uniform non-standard units (e.g. straws, wooden cubes, plastic weights, yogurt pots), or standard units (e.g. metre sticks, litre jugs).

74, 76 ◆ **Suggest suitable standard or uniform non-standard units and measuring equipment to estimate, then measure, a length, mass or capacity**, recording estimates and measurements as 'about 3 beakers full' or 'about as heavy as 20 cubes'.

78 ◆ Understand and use the vocabulary related to time. Order familiar events in time. Know the days of the week and the seasons of the year. Read the time to the hour or half hour on analogue clocks.

80–89 Shape and space

80 ◆ **Use everyday language to describe features of familiar 3-D and 2-D shapes**, including the cube, cuboid, sphere, cylinder, cone . . ., circle, triangle, square, rectangle . . ., referring to properties such as the shapes of flat faces, or the number of faces or corners . . . or the number and types of sides.

82 ◆ Make and describe models, patterns and pictures using construction kits, everyday materials, Plasticine . . . Fold shapes in half, then make them into symmetrical patterns. Begin to relate solid shapes to pictures of them.

86, 88 ◆ Use everyday language to describe position, direction and movement.

88 ◆ Talk about things that turn. Make whole turns and half turns. Use one or more shapes to make, describe and continue repeating patterns . . .

NOTES: ◆ Key objectives are highlighted in **bold type**.
◆ Page references are to the supplement of examples for Years 1, 2 and 3.

Figure 4.2 contd

Medium-term plans

You are given a blank grid to use for your medium-term planning if you wish, as shown in Figure 4.3

As you can see the grid indicates the topic to be taught organised as units of work. Figure 4.4 shows how one school sets out their weekly plan (short-term plan) on the basis of their medium-term plan.

Daily mathematics lessons are developed on the basis of the weekly plan. The structure of the daily lessons is suggested by the National Numeracy Strategy and more substantial guidance is provided in the *Framework*. Daily

Framework for teaching mathematics   Reception: Summer

Unit	Days	Pages	Topic	Objectives: children will be taught to . . .
1		2–10 11–13	Counting, reading and writing numbers Comparing and ordering numbers	
2		2–10 14–17	Counting, reading and writing numbers Adding and subtracting	
3		24–27 18–19	Shape and space Reasoning	
4		2–10 22–23	Counting, reading and writing numbers Measures	
5		2–10 14–17 20–21	Counting, reading and writing numbers Adding and subtracting Money and 'real life' problems	
6			**Assess and review**	
7		2–10 11–13	Counting, reading and writing numbers Comparing and ordering numbers	
8		2–10 14–17	Counting, reading and writing numbers Adding and subtracting	

Unit	Days	Pages	Topic	Objectives: children will be taught to ...
9		24–27 18–19	Shape and space Reasoning	
10		2–10 22–23	Counting, reading and writing numbers Measures, including time	
11		2–10 14–17 20–21	Counting, reading and writing numbers Adding and subtracting Money and 'real life' problems	
12			**Assess and review**	

Figure 4.3 Planning grid from the *Framework for teaching mathematics*

Maths topic: Addition   **MATHS WEEKLY PLAN**   Year Group: ....   Week: ....

Vocabulary: Add, plus, more, total, altogether signs +, =

Lesson	Objectives	Questions	INTRODUCTION mental/oral starter	MAIN ACTIVITY practical/written	PLENARY discussion
1	Extend understanding of addition as an operation. Use of appropriate vocabulary. Learn addition facts up to 10.	Can you explain what you understand by adding? Tell me all the addition facts up to 10.	Write on the board $8+2$ and ask children to give as many addition facts as possible. Focus on $2 + 8$ and $8 + 2$ being the same.	Demonstrate to the class how 2 sets of objects are combined to give a 'total'. Show addition on a number line. Worksheets (1) (2) (3) to groups.	Ask children to make up number sentences using 'addition'. Close your eyes and think about 2 addition facts; share.
2	Continue to develop understanding of addition. Highlight that the order does not matter when you add numbers.	Ask children to work out $\triangle + \square = 8$. What kind of questions. What can you say about the answer $15+12=$ and $12+15=$	Introduce $\triangle$ and $\square$ as two unknown numbers and to complete $\triangle + \square = 8$. Differentiated by size of nos.	Start with a discussion on adding 2 or 3 numbers; how the order in which you add them does not change the total: $3+6+1$. Play 3 dice game. Focus gp (2)	Ask children to think about and then share all the words they have learnt about addition. Encourage explanations.
3	Explore 3 numbers which add up to 100.	Can you think of 2 numbers which add up to 100; then: 3 numbers?	Let children work in pairs working out 2 numbers and then 3 numbers which add up to 100; Share with the whole class.	Explain '3 hops' to hundred game to the whole class. $(20) + (?) + (60) = 100$ Give out differentiated sheets with 2 or 3 hops with suitable Nos.	Play the 'function machine' game involving an 'input' number, addition operation and output No.

Figure 4.4 An example of a weekly plan

mathematics lesson plans must show **development**, highlight the appropriate mathematical language to be used, list **resources**, **key questions** and **organisational points**. Four lesson plans are provided later in this chapter for the reader to analyse and evaluate.

Who does what?

Completing the teaching grids is the class teacher's responsibility; it is the class teacher who should select one or two teaching objectives for each unit of work and decide the order in which they are taught. The aim is to make sure that all children have had some experience of covering all the objectives.

Whilst completing the blank grids, care should be taken in choosing a realistic number of objectives for a given time, including some kind of revision of previous concepts and some concepts which provide new learning. It makes sense to include concepts which are related, so that the inter-connections can be highlighted.

Another important point is emphasised in the *Framework* – evaluating the medium-term plan. At the end of each unit of work the work should be assessed, based on the teacher's assessment of the pupils. A simple system of coding or highlighting is recommended in the *Framework* to monitor whether:

◆ pupils have responded well and have met the objectives in full;

◆ pupils were responsive but the objectives still needed attention;

◆ an objective was not covered, or pupils did not meet it.

In practice this would mean that a teacher may highlight an objective in one colour if she felt that the objective had been well received and in another colour if a significant number of children experienced problems with it. There is an added advantage to this process; whilst this process is carried out, the teacher is also collecting information about individual children. The information collected can be used for further assessment or for considering future action. We will return to this topic in the section on assessment.

The highlighted grids are useful for another purpose. It offers an effective system for monitoring the progress throughout in the school. The information helps towards planning in subsequent terms and years. It also provides an evaluation system for the mathematics co-ordinator and the headteacher.

Evaluating your weekly plan

The basis for the daily plan is your short-term, or weekly plan. So it makes sense to consider what a good weekly plan should contain before considering daily planning. In the context of the National Numeracy Strategy, the following criteria are appropriate. A good weekly plan will:

♦ have clear objectives;

♦ highlight the activities to be taught during the daily lesson;

♦ include brief organisational structure and identify focus groups;

♦ list key questions and identify key vocabulary relating to the teaching content;

♦ list resources;

♦ outline questions for the first and final parts of the lesson;

♦ include possible extensions either as homework or for other times – say within another subject teaching (e.g. geography);

♦ have a balance of type of activities – skills, illustrations of concepts, problem solving and so on;

♦ be realistic in the amount of content to be covered.

Do we use published schemes for the daily lesson?

My own thinking is that the emphasis will change. For many years official reports have criticised teachers for their over-reliance on text books. It seems to me that as teachers become familiar with the Framework they will easily be able to incorporate text book ideas in to their weekly and daily plans. The shift will change, in that it will be the teachers who will plan and teach with commercial schemes providing the support, rather than commercial schemes driving the teaching. One will need to be careful to select only what is needed to deliver the teaching plan. The practice of making children do several pages of sums, irrespective of whether they need to or not, I believe, will come to an end. This will be a very welcome change.

The daily mathematics lesson

This is the stage where all the planning and preparation are put into practice. This is about the day-to-day teaching of mathematics.

The Framework offers the following guidelines on teaching the daily mathematics lesson, based on the National Numeracy Strategy:

♦ mathematics should be taught every day;

♦ there must be direct teaching and interactive oral work with the whole class and groups;

♦ mental mathematics must have a high profile in mathematics teaching;

◆ as far as possible, all pupils should be engaged in mathematics relating to a common theme.

Guidance is also offered, in the *Framework*, on how to plan a typical lesson. As the features of the three-part lesson will have a major influence on what happens in the classroom, the guidance in the *Framework* is presented below. This guidance will also provide a point of reference for the next section of this chapter.

Oral work and mental calculation

The first 5 to 10 minutes of a lesson can be used in a variety of ways to rehearse and sharpen skills, sometimes focusing on the skills that will be needed in the main part of the lesson. On different days you might choose to do one or more of these:

◆ *counting in steps of different sizes, including chanting as a whole class and counting round the class;*

◆ *practising mental calculations and the rapid recall of number facts in varied ways (for example, by playing an interactive number game, by giving examples of 'a number one less than a multiple of 5' or 'a calculation with the answer 12');*

◆ *figuring out new facts from known facts and explaining the strategies used;*

◆ *building on a previous strategy, and then developing it;*

◆ *identifying facts which children can learn by heart and discussing ways of remembering them;*

◆ *reviewing an activity done at home;*

In this first part of the lesson you need to:

◆ *get off to a clear start and maintain a brisk pace;*

◆ *provide a variety of short oral and mental activities throughout each week;*

◆ *prepare a good range of open and closed questions to ask the class;*

◆ *ensure that all children can see you easily and can and do take part;*

◆ *target individuals, pairs or small groups with particular questions;*

◆ *use pupils' responses to make an informal assessment of their progress;*

◆ *brief any support staff to position themselves and give discreet help to any children who need particular support;*

◆ *avoid disruption from too much movement of pupils about the room;*

◆ *avoid running over time and move smoothly to the next part of the lesson.*

The main teaching input and pupil activities

The main part of the lesson provides time for:

◆ introducing a new topic, consolidating previous work or extending it;

◆ developing vocabulary, using correct notation and terms and learning new ones;

◆ using and applying concepts and skills.

In this part of the lesson you need to:

◆ make clear to the class what they will learn;

◆ make links to previous lessons, or to work in other subjects;

◆ tell pupils what work they will do, how long it should take, what, if anything, they need to prepare for the plenary session and how they are to present it;

◆ maintain pace and give pupils a deadline for completing their work.

When you are working directly with the **whole class** you need to:

◆ demonstrate and explain using a board, flip chart, computer or OHP;

◆ involve pupils interactively through carefully planned questioning;

◆ ensure that pupils with particular learning needs in mathematics are supported effectively with appropriate resources and wall displays, and adult help;

◆ identify and correct any misunderstandings or forgotten ideas, using mistakes as positive teaching points;

◆ highlight the meaning of any new vocabulary, notation or terms, and get pupils to repeat these and use them in their discussions and written work;

◆ ask pupils to offer their methods and solutions to the whole class for discussion.

When you are working directly with **groups** you need to:

◆ have a manageable number of groups (usually a maximum of four), so that you know what each group should be doing at any time;

◆ decide how groups will be introduced to tasks and how the group work will end;

◆ control the degree of differentiation (for example, provide tasks on the same theme and usually at no more than three levels of difficulty);

◆ provide activities, tasks and resources that don't involve children in a long wait for turns and which keep them all interested, motivated and on-task;

◆ sit and work intensively with one or two of the groups, not flit between them all;

◆ brief any support staff or adult helpers about their role, making sure that they have plenty to do with the pupils they are assisting and will not interrupt you;

◆ avoid interruption by pupils by making sure that those working independently in a group know where to find further resources, what to do before asking you for help and what to do if they finish early.

When you are providing work for **individuals or pairs** you need to:

◆ keep the class working on related activities, exercises or problems;

◆ target individuals or pairs for particular questioning and support;

◆ during paired work, encourage discussion and co-operation between pupils.

The plenary session

The plenary is an important part of the lesson. It is a time when you can help pupils to assess their developing knowledge and skills against any targets they have been set and to see for themselves the progress they are making. It is also a time when you can relate mathematics to their work in other subjects: for example, how their work on calculation will be used in science, or how their measuring skills will be practised in physical education.

For example, this part of the lesson can be used to:

◆ ask pupils to present and explain their work, or mark a written exercise done individually during the lesson, so that you can question pupils about it, assess it informally and rectify any misconceptions or errors;

◆ discuss and compare the efficiency of pupils' different methods of calculation;

◆ help pupils to generalise a rule from examples generated by different groups, pairs or individuals;

◆ draw together what has been learned, reflect on what was important about the lesson, summarise key facts, ideas and vocabulary, and what needs to be remembered;

◆ discuss the problems that can be solved using the ideas and skills that have been learned;

◆ make links to other work and discuss briefly what the class will go on to do next;

◆ remind pupils about their personal targets and highlight the progress made;

◆ provide tasks for pupils to do at home to extend or consolidate their class work.

In this part of the lesson you need to:

◆ have a clear idea of the purpose of the plenary session and what you want to achieve in it;

◆ make sure that the main part of the lesson does not over-run, so that there is enough time for the plenary;

◆ plan carefully how pupils are to present their work, if they are to do this, and how long it will take;

◆ bring the lesson to a close and evaluate its success.

Different models of daily mathematics lessons

The sample daily mathematics lessons presented below were prepared by groups of teachers who were on our numeracy courses. In designing these plans, teachers were told to take into account both the recommendations of the Numeracy Strategy and the elements of 'good practice' in teaching and learning discussed during 'teaching numeracy' sessions at the University. Teachers were told that they would be asked to present their plans to the rest of the group; the purpose of this was two-fold. First, evaluating other people's work encourages us to examine our own beliefs and practices and this should lead to reflection and refinement of ideas. Secondly, these plans would exemplify the range of activities that can be used in the daily lesson. This must alleviate some teachers' worries that they have to re-invent mathematics teaching and seek new ideas and activities.

Three lesson plans are given. Consider them carefully and make notes about them. You may want to refer to the guidelines for the three-part daily lesson, shown below, to see if or how these lesson plans match the recommendations in the Framework.

Daily mathematics lesson one – Year 1

Learning objectives:

◆ Practising addition of numbers with totals up to 12.

◆ Teach children that when they add two numbers the order in which they are added does not matter.

◆ Re-arranging numbers may make addition easier.

Key words:
Add, plus, total, altogether, re-arrange, re-order

Resources:
Beans, dice marked 1 to 6, counters, grids with numbers 2–12

Introduction:
Let the children be seated in such a way that everyone can see what is happening. Show the children two sets of beans, say one set of six and the other a set of four. Ask them to tell you how many there are altogether. Invite responses. Ask them to explain how they got the answer. Repeat this a few times encouraging children to share their solutions and methods. Through targeted questioning find out if they are using the most efficient method for adding numbers. Do they know that the order of the numbers does not matter when you add two numbers? Highlight this point and ask some questions for the children to see this point and use this principle.

Key questions:
What is 5 + 5?
What do you get if you add 3 + 5; what if you add 5 + 3?
What can you say about the answer when you add 5 + 6 and 6 + 5?

Main activity:
Tell the children that they are going to play a dice game in groups of 4. Each child is given a few counters and a grid marked with numbers 2–12. In turn, each player throws two dice together and adds up the scores. The total obtained is then covered on his or her board. The player who covers all or the most numbers on the grid wins. Tell the children that they need to add the two scores fast and to remember what they have learnt previously; that they could re-order numbers to make addition easier. The whole class plays the game; support is provided as the teacher circulates. During her visit to each group she encourages them to try and remember the number facts rather than try to 'count on' each time.

Plenary:
Ask children to think about the game they had been playing for a minute. Ask the following questions.

◆ What have you learnt from playing the dice game?

◆ What new number facts do you know now that you did not know before the game?

◆ Add 4 + 5 =; 6 + 3 =; 2 + 5 =; 2 + 6 = and so on

◆ Now try adding three and four numbers: 4 + 3 + 1 =; 6 + 3 + 5 =; 5 + 2 + 5 + 6 =

Homework:
What numbers can you get by adding three dice? Ask the children to bring their ideas in for the following day's lesson.

Daily mathematics lesson two – Year 3

Learning objectives:

- ◆ The ideas of multiplication, division and the relationship between the two operations.

- ◆ Introduce the concept of factors, divisibility and remainders.

- ◆ Meet prime numbers.

Key words:

Lots of, groups of, left over, times tables, remainder, factors, divisible, multiple, prime number

Resources:

Small cubes or butter beans, score sheets as shown, 0–100 cards

Introduction:

- ◆ Ask children to count in 2s, 3s, 4s as a class activity.

- ◆ The teacher then puts her fingers up one by one; for each finger children must count on in a previously decided jump, say jumps of 5, so for 1 finger 5, 2 fingers 10, for 3 fingers the response will be 15 and so on.

- ◆ Practise different size jumps, up and down, for about 10 minutes.

Main activity:

- ◆ The teacher writes a number, say 16 on the board and asks the children what number jumps will enable them to land on 16 – yes, 2, 4, and 8. Repeat for 12, 24, 15, 30.

- ◆ Invite three children to come to the front. Let them take a handful of beans each and count them. First discuss the way the beans have been counted. Were their methods different? Was one method better than the others? (Did they group the beans in some way, or count in ones?)

Introduce the game with the three volunteers playing from the front. (This game can be played in groups of three or four.) Each person, in turn, takes a handful of beans and counts them quickly using the fastest method and asks the questions: can this number be grouped into 2s, 3s, 4s and 5s without any left over? On an OHT, show a scoring board and fill it in during the demonstration game. Copies of blank score sheets should be available.

- ◆ Ask selected children what the score would be if a bigger number from the pack of 0–100 cards is picked, say 42, what will be the score?

Sample score–sheet

Name:

Number of beans	In sets of 2	In sets of 3	In sets of 4	In sets of 5	Score
14	2	0	0	0	2
15	0	3	0	5	8
17	0	0	0	0	0
24	2	3	4	0	9
					Total = 19

◆ Ask if they know the word used to describe a number which goes into a number without any left over – the word 'multiple' is introduced; in the same way, through targeted questioning, select children to name and explain factors, and prime numbers; if they don't know the words, here is your golden opportunity.

◆ Send the children away to play the game: Children who don't need to (physically) group the beans can use number cards for the game whilst others take handfuls each time. Fix a time when the game must stop.

◆ The teacher decides to circulate amongst the groups with two main objectives at this stage: this is an excellent activity to assess children, secondly this activity provides a great opportunity for teaching or reinforcing words such as factors, multiples and so on.

◆ Be prepared to have larger number cards for those who need extension.

Plenary:

◆ Ask children to discuss, in pairs, to decide and prepare an explanation for the question: if you could choose any number between 1 and 40 for a handful, what number would you choose? What if you could have any number between 0 and 100?

◆ Ask carefully chosen children to list and explain new mathematical words they have learnt.

◆ Ask for volunteers to put up a display of the new words during the week. Some of the work for the display could be done at home.

Include some word problems in the display for others to solve: *Which number between 20 and 34 has the most number of factors? Is it true that 60 is the best number to pick between 0 and 100? Why do you think some children call the numbers 17, 31 and 37 'horrible numbers'?*

Daily mathematics lesson three – Year 6

Learning objectives:

◆ Reinforce fractions and percentages lessons learnt previously.

◆ Highlight the relationship between fractions and percentages.

◆ Solve problems which involve working out percentages.

Key words:

Fraction words, halves, thirds, quarters, two thirds and others as appropriate, percentage, equal to

Introduction:

◆ Tell the children they are going to revisit what they have learnt about fractions and percentages.

◆ Ask questions, enquiring periodically, what methods are used to work these out.
   – What is half of 46, 50% of 46, a third of 40?
   – How would they describe a 'quarter', an eighth?
   – What is $\frac{2}{3}$ of £36? $\frac{4}{5}$ of 200?
   – If £25 is 25% of my savings, what are my total saving?

As a whole class activity, fill in the conversion chart on the board using appropriate entries as preparation for the main activity: an example is given below.

Fraction	Percentage
1/2	50%
?	20%
?	75%
3/4	?
1/10	?
2/5	?
?	60%

Main activity:

Explain to the children they are going to solve some problems which involve using what they have learnt during the introduction. Ask them to use the most efficient method to solve the problems. Tell them it helps to write down the steps in their calculation because they can see where they are going and to make a rough estimate of what the answer may be like.

Children are given sheets with some word problems. They work in differentiated groups using the 'problems' sheets which the teacher has selected for them. They are asked to show the methods they used by recording.

Examples of problems:

◆ What is 50% of £48?

◆ You have to pay 25% deposit for an electronic game to reserve it. If the game costs £98.88, how much do you have to pay as a deposit?

◆ What amount must you pay for an item costing £480, if there is reduction of $12\frac{1}{2}$ % in the sale?

◆ How would you work out $17\frac{1}{2}$ % of £2000?

Plenary:

◆ Using a sheet of examples from newspapers and catalogues which have 'percentages' and 'fractions', perhaps invite the children to work out the new prices.

| 50% off for these goods | 1/3 off all items | 5% off all toys |

◆ Finish with a poster which says: If you could have a choice of $\frac{3}{7}$ or 40% of 350 sweets which would you choose? Give a reason. Ask the children to work this out.

Homework:

Collect two or three examples of 'fraction' or 'percentage' reductions for items, from newspapers or magazines, and bring them in for Friday's lesson. Get parents to help to find them.

Evaluating the daily lesson plans

At this point it is useful to consider the plans in the light of the guidance given in the *Framework* and to make comments. For example, you may want to include more open-ended questions in the introduction, you may think that the pace is too slow, or repetitive or that the plan is unrealistic.

Undertaking this kind of analysis will be useful when you are planning with your colleagues. That way you are likely to end up with a well thought-out plan. Eventually, these lesson plans will build up to a collection of tried and tested ideas.

Variety of presentations

A close study of the recommend structure for the daily mathematics lesson shows that a variety of presentations are needed in order to address all the objectives. This will pose a challenge for some teachers. The following examples of activities have been used successfully by teachers who have attempted to select a variety of activities for their daily mathematics lesson.

Investigating in the 'main part' of the activity

Halina, a Year 2 teacher, asked her children to investigate the following problem, in pairs, during the main teaching activity:

> You have lots and lots of 3p and 5p stamps. Which totals, from 1 to 20, can you make? You have lots of stamps and can use as many as you wish.

The main objective of this lesson was to provide the children with opportunities to use and apply their numerical skills, selecting and using both appropriate materials and mathematics, reasoning and systematic work.

Priyanka, age six, as can be seen opposite, started recording each of the numbers beginning with 1 and then decided to create a number square for her recordings. Her explanation for the ticks was interesting too:

> I started ticking all the numbers in the 'threes and fives' jumps and then I got stuck because number eight works too. Then I had to work those out, that got difficult. Me and friend worked them out together.

Addressing children's misconceptions during the 'introduction'

Addressing children's mistakes and misconceptions is an important part of teaching numeracy. As part of the introduction to the daily lessons David, a Year 5 teacher, regularly encourages his children to talk about their methods. One day he decided to ask his children to check a set of sums done by an 'imaginary' child of their age. They had to say whether the sums were right or wrong within 10 minutes, without using pencil and paper; this meant estimating, reasoning and checking. The sums shown opposite were given on the board – done by an imaginary child called Jason.

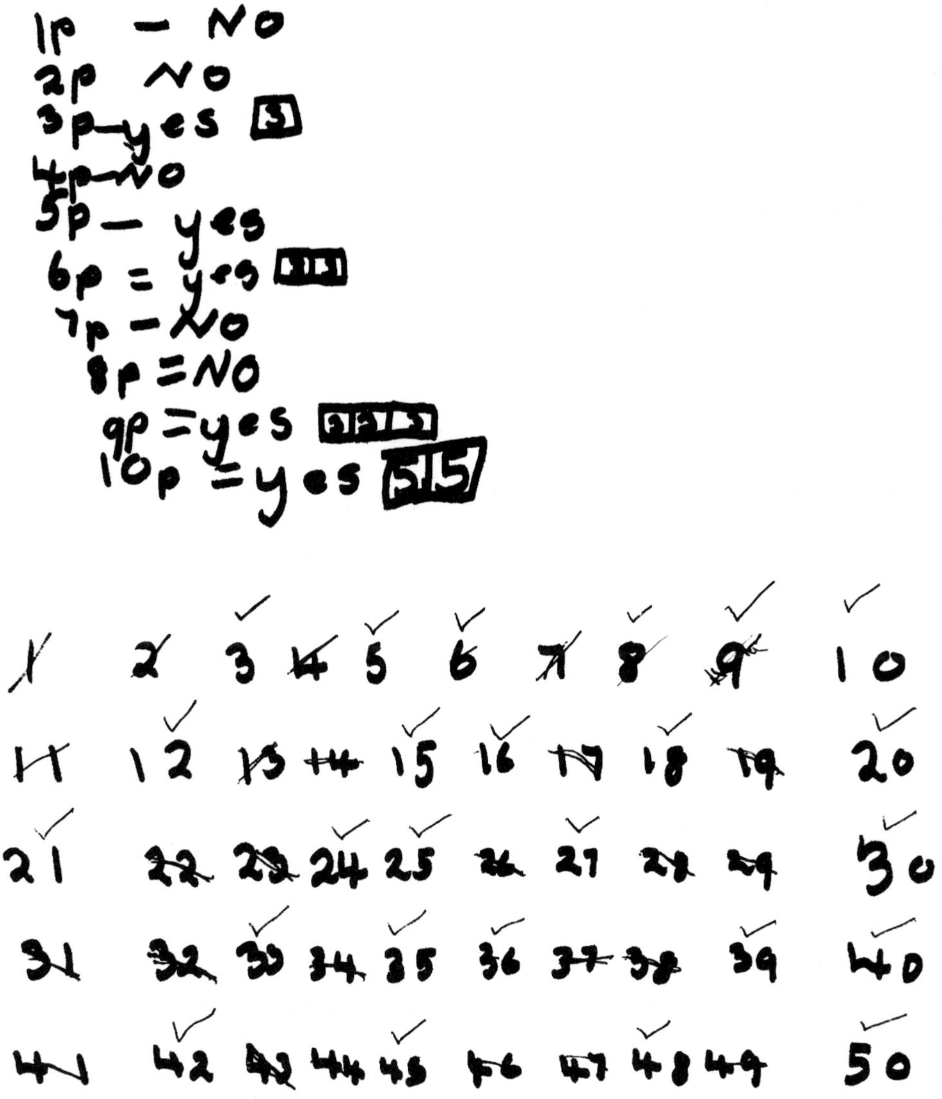

1p – NO
2p NO
3p – yes [3]
4p – NO
5p – yes
6p = yes [111]
7p – NO
8p = NO
9p = yes [3 3 3]
10p = yes [5 5]

1 2 3 4 5 6 7 8 9 10
11 12 13 14 15 16 17 18 19 20
21 22 23 24 25 26 27 28 29 30
31 32 33 34 35 36 37 38 39 40
41 42 43 44 45 46 47 48 49 50

Priyanka's work

Jason's work — please check

$906 + 6800 + 4 = 7710$

$2500 - 349 = 1141$

$1806 \times 5 = 9030$

$21 \times 79 = 1659$

$200 \times 43 = 1060$

6995 divided by 5 = 111 r = 5

The teacher, David, talked about the amount of interest and discussion this activity generated during the lesson. Children analysed the answers, estimated what the answers should be like and considered possible reasons for the mistakes.

Getting children to ask questions during an 'introduction'

The next example is based on a familiar activity, but conducted in perhaps a novel way. Children in a Year 1 class were told, during an introductory session, that on that day they would be asking the questions. The dartboard activity was explained to them.

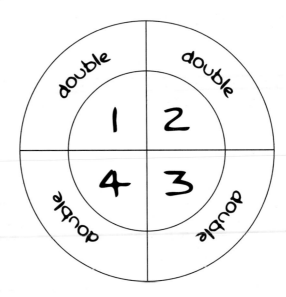

The teacher explained that each of them would have three counters which they could use as darts. Using an OHT of the Dartboard, she asked one child to come forward and show where she would place the three darts to get score of 9. For the rest of the time it was up to the children to make up the questions. Initially, the children were baffled and showed much anxiety; one child, almost in tears, said, 'but it is the teacher who asks the questions, not children'. However, after a few minutes questions came flooding in:

◆ How can you get a score of 12?

◆ Can you get a score of 2?

◆ What is the largest score you can make?

◆ What is the lowest score you can make?

◆ Can you make a 7?

Investigating consecutive numbers for the main part of the lesson and preparing for the plenary

The final example shows a lesson in a Year 3 class in which children were asked to investigate the following question, during the main activity. This came after a mental addition session.

Find out what consecutive numbers are.

You can make 15 by adding 2 consecutive numbers: $7 + 8 = 15$. You can make 15 by adding 5 consecutive numbers: $1 + 2 + 3 + 4 + 5 = 15$

Can you make all the numbers up to 20 by adding consecutive numbers?

Children were told they would be given A3 sheets of paper on which to record their findings, 5 minutes before the end of the lesson so that they could present them in the plenary session. Planned plenaries are more effective!

Evaluating your teaching

We have been considering 'good practice' in teaching numeracy throughout this book. Therefore, you should be able to draw up your own list of what constitutes a 'good' lesson. The list of criteria for evaluating your teaching, provided as part of the training for the implementation of the National Numeracy Strategy (DfEE, 1999), may be helpful. The list is given below.

Effective teaching involves:

1   high expectations and clear objectives – conveyed to the children;
2   well structured lessons and a suitable pace;
3   a high proportion of direct teaching, with resources used well to model methods;
4   daily oral and mental work;
5   the use of correct mathematical vocabulary and notation;
6   effective differentiation and questioning in whole-class work to involve all children and make informal assessment of their progress;
7   manageable differentiation in group work (linked group tasks, no more than 3 levels);
8   well-organised group work, so the teacher can teach without interruption;
9   varied opportunities for children to demonstrate and explain, do practical work, discuss, practise, solve problems;
10   purposeful plenary: key learning points reinforced, misconceptions dealt, links made to other topics and subjects, homework set;
11   support staff deployed effectively.

Assessing children's learning

The third element in the planning, teaching and assessing cycle is assessment. The description of assessment provided in the Report of the Task Group on Assessment and Testing (DES, 1987) provides a good starting point for this section. TGAT has this to say:

> Promoting children's learning is a principal aim of schools. Assessment lies at the heart of this process. It can provide a framework in which educational objectives may be set, and pupils progress chartered and expressed. It can yield a basis for planning the next educational steps in response to children's needs. (para 3)

The Framework acknowledges the important role of assessment in the learning process and maintains that, if assessment is to be useful, the information collected needs to be manageable. It also emphasises the need for consistency across the school.

How do we assess children?

Before considering assessment in the context of the National Numeracy Strategy, we need to think about the ways in which we assess children. We assess children in the following ways:

◆ **by listening to what they say**: in their individual conversations with the teacher, in group and class discussions;

◆ **by observing what they do**: how they do something, say counting a collection of objects, or what decisions they make in selecting a method of calculation or for solving a problem. Through observation a teacher can often pick up much information about children's attitudes and what they find enjoyable or dislike;

◆ **by analysing written work**: this involves looking at what children put down on paper, such as strategies and procedures they use they use for calculations. A significant amount of information can be gathered if you were to spend two or three minutes with a child while you are marking his or her sums. Children's mistakes often provide teachers with insights into their ways of thinking and their misconceptions.

Formative assessment

All the ways of assessing described above help the teacher to build up an effective formative system and on-going, day-to-day collection of information which is different from the summative assessment carried out at the end of term, end of Year or end of Key Stage. Much of the information for formative assessment can be collected as part of the daily teaching in the classroom. This makes it manageable.

Now let us explore what this involves. How does it work in practice? How do we assess children's mathematics learning in the classroom? At this point, it may be useful to consider how formative assessment can take place at different stages in the implementation of the mathematics programme, as set out in the *Framework*.

The planning stage

Planning records should show clear objectives which reflect recommendations in the *Framework*. Daily lessons should take account of both informal and formal notes kept on children's learning in order to address their individual needs. Sharing the learning intentions with the children at the beginning of a lesson helps them to share the responsibility for their learning and to maintain a better focus on what is taught.

The teaching stage

The *Framework* places much emphasis on interactive teaching; this provides the teacher with many opportunities to make assessments of children. Consider a daily mathematics lesson. During the introduction, much of the work is oral work; children communicate their learning during these sessions, either through answering questions targeted at them or in general discussions. The teacher gains insights into children's mental strategies, the efficiency of their methods and their misconceptions. It is equally important to notice the child who shows anxiety or who does not want to participate. Action needs to be taken in all these cases.

During the main teaching activity, the teacher may focus on one or two groups or circulate amongst all the children. In either case, this would be the time to do a few minutes of focused observation. You may observe a child who is having special difficulties or showing frustration. Just a few minutes of focused observation can often provide you with a wealth of information and, as it is part of the daily lesson, it does not involve extra work. You will only need to keep notes of anything special.

A systematic formative sampling record can be very useful for assessing and recording information on individual children, when you feel the need for a formal assessment, perhaps when you need to provide evidence for requesting special provision or when a parent is concerned, or to construct Individual Educational Plans for selected children. When children come to you to get their work marked, there is an opportunity for discussing any points which need attention, or which may be useful for diagnostic purposes. If the marking is not done in the presence of the child, it is worth considering the nature of your feedback. Think about what message you want the child to get from your response. Focusing on one or two points that need improvement is better than a page of crosses. If the page is always full of ticks, that also needs consideration.

During the plenary there are more opportunities to gather information about whether the children have learnt what you wanted them to learn, how they have learnt the ideas and whether there are gaps in what they have learnt. In addition to the discussions during plenary sessions, it is a good idea to encourage children to reflect on their own leaning. There is increasing evidence, some based on the work I have undertaken, that self-assessment – oral or written – can enhance children's achievement. I have often encouraged children to keep mathematics journals in which they are asked, periodically, to make entries about what new ideas they have learnt, construct an on-going mathematical glossary and so on. The process of self-assessment can be very useful in target setting for individual children. Targets set against a child's own awareness of his or her needs have a better chance of being achieved.

Before considering different forms of assessment and recording systems, here is an exercise for you to do. Study the collection of mistakes shown opposite and make two types of comments:

◆ What are the possible reasons for each mistake?

◆ How would you help the child?

This should be a useful exercise for you do with your colleagues. If you can identify possible mistakes or misconceptions in advance, you can be proactive in trying to address them in your teaching. Mistakes can often be reduced in this way.

Some examples of assessment and recording systems

The following formative methods of assessment and record keeping can be used as part of the information gathering about children's numerical competence. For effective teacher assessment you need to use a range of systems. The type of assessment you would use and the record you keep should depend upon the purpose.

Leanne, age 5

$$8 + 5 = 12$$

counted and wrote 31

Garry , age 6

$$\begin{array}{r} 46 \\ + 11 \\ \hline 57 \checkmark \end{array} \qquad \begin{array}{r} 13 \\ + 4 \\ \hline 8 \end{array} \qquad \begin{array}{r} 20 \\ + 18 \\ \hline 38 \checkmark \end{array} \qquad \begin{array}{r} 24 \\ + 3 \\ \hline 9 \end{array}$$

David, age 9

$$\begin{array}{r} 43 \\ \times \quad 4 \\ \hline 181 \\ 2 \end{array} \qquad \begin{array}{r} 37 \\ \times \quad 6 \\ \hline 204 \\ 2 \end{array} \qquad \begin{array}{r} 2\,4\,3\,6 \\ - 3\,6\,7 \\ \hline 1\,7\,9 \end{array} \qquad \begin{array}{r} 4009 \\ - \quad 117 \\ \hline 1\,99\,12 \end{array}$$

Debbie, age 10

$$\begin{array}{r} 168 \\ \times \quad 6 \\ \quad 4 \\ \hline 848 \\ 2 \end{array} \qquad \begin{array}{r} 374 \\ \times \quad 6 \\ \quad 2 \\ \hline 1944 \\ 1 \end{array} \qquad \begin{array}{r} 025 \quad r=0 \\ 10 \overline{\smash{)}\,2500} \end{array}$$

James, age 10, used a calculator and got:

$$£74.91 - 67p = £7.91$$

Lee , age 11

$$3\frac{1}{5} + 2\frac{3}{4} = 5\frac{4}{9}$$

$$6.7 \times 10 = 6.70$$

Figure 4.5 Children's mistakes collected from their mathematics books

General monitoring records

For the day-to-day assessment of children's learning, the *Framework*
recommends a 'class record' of key objectives. This as can be seen in Figure
4.6 which is a summary sheet for the whole class. It lists the key objectives
on one side and the pupils' names along the other side.

Key objectives: Year 4	Raj	Anna
Use symbols correctly, including <, >, =		
Round any positive integer less than 1000 to the nearest 10 or 100		
Recognise simple fractions that are several parts of a whole, and mixed numbers; recognise the equivalence of simple fractions		
Use known number facts and place value to add or subtract mentally, including any pair of two-digit whole numbers		
Carry out column addition and subtraction of two integers less than 1000, and column addition of more than two such integers		
Know by heart facts for the 2, 3, 4, 5 and 10 multiplication tables		
Derive quickly division facts corresponding to the 2, 3, 4, 5 and 10 multiplication tables		
Find remainders after division		
Know and use the relationships between familiar units of length, mass and capacity		
Classify polygons, using criteria such as number of right angles, whether or not they are regular, symmetry properties		
Choose and use appropriate number operations and ways of calculating (mental, mental with jottings, pencil and paper) to solve problems		
Other		

Figure 4.6 Class record of key objectives

The simplicity of this makes it attractive and the fact that there are only a few key objectives per year makes the work manageable. It is recommended that these records are updated every six weeks or so. Some teachers have found this a useful system for recording the attainment of children, by using different colour highlighters or a differentiated tick system (say a tick for evidence of 'good understanding' or a crossed tick for 'partial understanding' or a blank for 'no understanding'. Some notes may be kept to supplement the information on children who warrant special attention for any reason.

Formative teacher assessment record

A sampling record as suggested by Mitchell and Koshy (1995), is very useful for carrying out structured observations of children's learning. This is particularly useful for diagnostic purposes. As you can see in Figure 4.7 the planning, teaching and assessing record is reflected in this system. Figure 4.8 shows a completed record for Natalie.

Possible Outcomes		
why have I planned this activity?		
Account	Interpretation	Action
what actually happened?	what does this tell me about the learner?	how does this help my next planning?
what did the child do, say, write or make?	what does the child know, understand or do?	what might I plan next?

Figure 4.7 Planning, teaching and assessing sampling record

The possible outcomes section in Figure 4.7 lists the learning objectives of the activity to be observed. The teacher may decide to focus on one or two key ideas for observation. In the 'account' section you would record the key elements of what the child said, did or wrote. The interpretation is more complex and needs careful thought. Some teachers have found it useful to discuss this section with colleagues or with the special needs co-ordinator, especially if the child is being considered for special needs provision.

FORMATIVE TEACHER ASSESSMENT RECORD   Y1 ☐   Y2 ☑   Y3 ☐

Y4 ☐   Y5 ☐   Y6 ☐

Name: Natalie

Date: June 99

Activity: Target 30 – Collecting units and exchanging for 'tens'

Possible Outcomes
Recognition of numbers on dice Addition of scores on two dice Exchanging 10 units for a 'ten' and moving it to the 'left' column Showing understanding of place value.

Account	Interpretation	Action
Recognised all the numbers on the dice. When adding 'six' and 'three', started counting from 'one' to, 'six' and then 'three' more to get 9. Knows 9 add 1 make 10 and to make a ten stick and move it to the 'tens' column. After moving a 'ten' to the left and counting the units in the 'units' column, looked confused. couldn't tell '1' ten and '2' units made twelve.	Good recognition of numbers 1 to 6. Has not grasped the idea that you can count on from 6 to add 6 and 3. Can make a 'ten' stick and move it to the left – this may be 'copying' what the others did! She has no clear understanding of place-value system and the role of the 'columns'.	I need to teach Natalie that you can count on from the first number when adding two numbers. Natalie needs more experience with number bonds, making 'tens' in different ways and then do preparatory work on place-value.

Comments:

Go slow here. Natalie knows quite a bit; Somehow it all needs pulling together before pushing her to learn tens and units. I overestimated her capability with number bonds and addition of numbers.

Figure 4.8   Natalie's record

The action column is a very important part of this system of recording. As Mitchell and Koshy point out:

> Effective teacher assessment not only involves looking closely at children's learning and offering some interpretations, but also moving to the next stage — of making use of the information gathered to plan subsequent learning experiences. In this way, the action section of the Formative Teacher Assessment record completes the assessment cycle by taking you back to the planning stage. (p. 54)

What action needs to be taken will certainly depend on the evidence recorded in the account section and what the interpretations are. The notes collected through focused observation can also be very helpful when meeting parents.

Class and group tests

Teachers in two Local Education Authorities I am working with, have found the use of short tests, at the end of a unit of work, worthwhile. A reward system of certificates and treats has also been built into this scheme. A short oral and written test is given to all the children. The performance in these tests not only helps to monitor the level of the children's understanding of what is taught, it also highlights any areas which are not understood and any misconceptions children may have before it is too late.

Multiple choice

For each of the questions below, four options are given. Circle the correct answer and be prepared to justify your reason for the choice.

Which of the following in a prime number?

A. 99
B. 91
C. 97
D. 93

Which of the following could be the correct answer to the sum 203 ✕ 31

A. 693
B. 6300
C. 700
D. 60 000

Two thirds of £360.00 is:

A. £180.00
B. £320.00
C. £240.00
D. £260.00

The number with the highest number of factors is:

A. 20
B. 32
C. 9
D. 24

Figure 4.9 Multiple choice test

Short 'Multiple Choice' tests, as shown in Figure 4.9 also enable teachers to gather information about children's learning. Barbara, a Year 5 teacher, explained:

> I never expected such enthusiasm for any kind of test before. My children love Multiple Choice tests. I gave them one in the first week of the term, they were so keen and I was sure the questions made them think, so I decided to give them a test every month on topics we have covered. They really are useful.

Although summative tests such as the Standard Assessment Tasks (SATS) are useful and can supply information about children's learning, it is the day-to-day formative assessment of children which will enhance the quality of your daily teaching.

Summary

This chapter dealt with three interrelated aspects of teaching mathematics – planning, teaching and assessing. Starting with the guidance provided by the *Framework* for teaching mathematics, issues relating to long-, medium- and short-term planning were explored. Sample daily lessons were included for the reader to consider how they meet the requirements of the recommended structure of the daily mathematics lesson. The chapter concluded with a discussion of effective ways of assessing children's mathematical learning.

Chapter 5

Using Information and Communications Technology to develop numeracy

The aim of this chapter is to examine the role of Information and Communications Technology (ICT) in developing children's numeracy skills. Two principles have always guided me when considering the role of ICT. First, ICT has much to offer teachers and pupils in the teaching and learning of mathematics and secondly, considering the fast rate at which technology is developing with applications in all fields of life, it is common sense to help our children to become proficient in the use of ICT. In this chapter some ways in which ICT can be used in schools to support the teaching of numeracy are explored.

Take a moment to list what you consider to be included in ICT. Compare your list with what is included in the *Framework* for teaching mathematics, where calculators, computers, audio-visual aids, tape-recorders, video-tapes and educational broadcasts are all included. The *Framework* also reminds us that we can use ICT in various ways to support teaching and motivate children's learning. Some suggestions for the effective use of ICT are also included.

This chapter looks at ways in which teachers have used ICT to enhance children's numerical competence. This is done in three sections: the role of calculators, the role of computers and a final, brief section which deals with other practical ways in which teachers have used other ICT resources.

The role of calculators

For the last 15 years there has a been a lively debate on the use of calculators. Many of us are familiar with a range of views, from 'calculators should carry a warning that they cause "brain power damage"' to 'calculators can enhance mathematical understanding'. No extensive research has been published about the use calculators in the UK, but useful suggestions have been made by the PrIME (Primary Initiative in Mathematics Education, 1989) project on the positive aspects of using calculators with children. Looking back, some very useful points were also made about the use of calculators in the Cockcroft Report (1982). As the views expressed in the Report are as relevant now as they were then, some of these are summarised in the following section. It would be useful for you to reflect on these, perhaps with a colleague, and write down your own views next to the following statements:

◆ There is widespread public concern about the use of calculators by children who have not mastered the traditional 'pencil and paper' methods of computation. It is feared that children who use calculators too early will not acquire fluency in computation nor confident recall of basic number facts.

◆ Some research studies carried out in the United States of America have reported improvements amongst children who used calculators in terms of attitudes, in personal computational skills and in understanding concepts in problem solving.

◆ The availability of a calculator in no way reduces the need for mathematical understanding on the part of the person using it. A calculator is of no use until decisions are made about which operations are to be used.

◆ Calculators are useful resources to illustrate 'number' ideas; for example, asking children to change number 502 to 5720 or to 57.2 reinforces place value.

◆ Children who use calculators are likely to meet decimals and negative numbers earlier than those who do not.

◆ The availability of calculators enables children to deal with larger numbers than would otherwise be possible.

◆ A calculator makes it possible to deal with 'real life' situations in problem solving.

The report does suggest that more work is needed before considering the extent to which calculators should be used in primary schools.

Although no extensive research focusing on the use of calculators has been published since, projects such as the Calculator Aware Number (CAN) have shown that children benefit from using calculators from the early stages of their learning. Duffin (1997) argues convincingly that the presence of calculators cannot be held responsible for any decline in standards. She draws our attention to the fact that Ofsted (1993) informed us that the skills of using a calculator have been neglected in a high percentage of schools and that in only a tenth of lessons calculators were used. From her personal experience of working with a large numbers of children, she maintains that, if calculators are used properly from an early age, they can greatly enrich the 'number' experience of learners. She also maintains that calculators seem to have a special quality to generate talk. Therefore, if care is taken about how to introduce and use calculators, they cannot be in conflict with the objectives of the Numeracy Strategy.

Duffin believes that much of the 'fear' of calculators is fuelled by the media telling us that calculators will 'rot the brain'. Thompson's arguments (TES, 1999) also help to inform those who may be confused by the conflicting reports which suggest that using calculators is responsible for the deficiencies in British children's number work. He puts forward evidence to show that this is not so. First, he points out that the School Curriculum and Assessment Authority's publication 'The Use of Calculators at Key Stages 1–3' (1997) and some Ofsted publications in fact suggest that pupil performance benefits from the proper use of calculators. Thompson also points out that in the recent Third International Mathematics and Science Survey (TIMSS) Singapore, with the highest reported use of calculators, did better than all the other countries which took part.

The Final Report of the Numeracy Task Force (DfEE, 1998) expresses the view that the use of calculators must be restricted to the later years of Key Stage 2 and that calculators should not be used for simple arithmetic, since children should learn both the mental and written calculations they need for life. The advice provided in the *Framework* is that:

> *Calculators offer a unique way of learning about numbers and the number system, place value, properties of numbers and fractions and decimals. (p. 8)*

A number of suggestions for using calculators to develop numeracy skills are provided in the *Framework*. The need for teaching children how to use a calculator and how to interpret the results is also emphasised.

I feel it may be useful for the reader to consider the list of suggestions, provided in the *Framework* about which calculator skills should be taught to children in Years 5 and 6. They are:

◆ Use, read, write and spell correctly words such as calculator, display, key, enter, clear, constant, recurring.

◆ Use the numbers, operations and equals keys and decimal points.

◆ Change accidental mistakes using the CE key.

◆ Key in, correctly, calculations involving money, and interpret results.

◆ Understand the sequence to carry out calculations involving more than one step; for example, the use of brackets.

◆ Develop an understanding and feel for the appropriate answer.

◆ Interpreting and rounding of answers.

◆ Use calculators to solve realistic problems by knowing which procedures and operations to use and how to input data which may not always be 'tidy'.

Teaching children how to use a calculator

Learning how to use a calculator efficiently and when to use it are important aspects of developing numeracy. Before introducing calculators to children, it may be useful for teachers to remind themselves about some aspects of their use. First, find out what type of calculator you have in your classroom and consider what type of calculator may be the most useful.

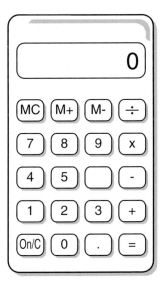

Most people are familiar with the digit keys:
the arithmetic signs:

1 2 3 4 5 6 7 8 9 0

$+$ $-$ $\times$ $\div$ and $=$

Is your calculator an *Arithmetic* or *Algebraic* calculator?

Try this: $4 + 2 \times 4 =$ if the answer is 24, you have an **arithmetic calculator**. This means your calculator performs the operations in the order in which you key them in. It works as if there is a bracket around $4 + 2$.

If, for the above calculation, your calculator gives you the answer 12, you have an **algebraic calculator**. In the latter case the calculator has multiplied 2 and 4 before adding 4. So, if you want to get the result 24 with an algebraic calculator, you will need to work out $(4 + 2) \times 4$. To do this without brackets you need to press $4 + 2 = \times 4 =$

This is a useful activity for children to do.

Does your calculator have a *constant* function?

> Switch the calculator on. Press: 3 + 2 = = = = *Watch what happens; if it produces* 5, 7, 9, 11, 13 *and so on, your calculator has the constant facility. Try the following if you want to find out if your calculator has a constant function key.*
>
> 30 − 5 = = = = *it should produce* 25, 20, 15, 10, 5, *etc.*
>
> 2 × 4 = = = = *do you get* 8, 16, 32, 64 *and so on?*
>
> 128 ÷ 2 = = = = *do you obtain* 64, 32, 16, 8 . . .?

Most calculators can do this for all 4 calculations. Some only do it for multiplication and division. Did you notice that for the operations +, − and ÷ the second number is the constant, whereas for ×, the first number is the constant?

A great facility for predicting number patterns!

How is your 'Key' expertise?

> ### The square root key
>
> *This gives you the square root of any number. Try pressing 4 followed by the square root key then try;* 16, 25, 81, 225, 10 000.

> ### The percentage key
>
> *The* %| *key is used to calculate percentage values; there are several different ways of doing this:*
>
> ◆ *say you want to find 25% of 248, press 248 × 25% (you don't need to press =)*
>
> ◆ *if you need to add 15% of £200 to £200, press 200 + 15%, or you could do it this way: 200 × 15% + =*
>
> ◆ *if you want to express 32 marks out of 60 as a %, press 32 − 40%*

Memory keys $\boxed{\text{M}+}$ $\boxed{\text{M}-}$ $\boxed{\text{MR}}$ $\boxed{\text{CM}}$

First Clear Memory

- ◆ *to perform the calculation* $(4 \times 6) + (5 \times 3)$ *press* 4×6 $\boxed{\text{M}+}$ 5×3 $\boxed{\text{M}+}$ $\boxed{\text{MR}}$

- ◆ *to perform a decimal operation* $(3.4 \times 6.2) - (12.6 - 3.2)$ *press* 3.4×6.2 $\boxed{\text{M}+}$ $12.6 - 3.2$ $\boxed{\text{M}-}$ $\boxed{\text{MR}}$.

Powers of numbers

To find squares and higher powers of numbers' if you have constant function

$5^2 = 5 \times = 25$
$5^3 = 5 \times = =$ $\qquad\qquad$ $5^4 = 5 \times = = =$

Clear Entry key – CE

This key cancels the last entry you have made. This is useful if you make a mistake; say you want to find 35×3 *but pressed* 35×2 *by mistake. Then use the CE key:*

$\boxed{35}$ $\boxed{\times}$ $\boxed{2}$ $\boxed{\text{CE}}$ $\boxed{3}$ $\boxed{=}$

try this a few times

The following section provides some practical examples of how teachers have used calculators to develop aspects of numeracy. Try these activities yourself, in pairs, small groups or teams to see how these activities can generate a great deal of discussion, estimating and reasoning.

Calculators to support understanding of place value

Calculators can support children in their understanding of place value, which is an important factor in children developing a 'feel' for number.

An activity such as 'Place Invader' promotes thinking about the values of digits being relative to their position in a number. For example consider the following activity:

An activity for two or three players

This can be adapted for the whole class using a calculator attached to an OHP. Display a list of numbers **563, 500, 570, 403,** and so on. Shoot each of the digits down one at a time by <u>subtracting</u>.

For example to reduce 563 to zero by subtracting one digit at a time, you would follow these steps:

563   **press −3 = 560**
         press −60 = 500
         press −500 = 0

Extensions: Use 4 digit numbers
         Shoot the numbers starting from the units or thousands
         Make up list of numbers for others to shoot down

To extend this to decimals and to highlight the effect of multiplying and dividing by 10 and 100 you could start with a number 5432.356 and say: the rule is that you can only shoot a number down in the units column. The process would be as follows:

Press the keys	Calculator display
5432.356	
−2	5430.356
÷10	543.0356
−3	540.0356
÷100	5.400356
−5	0.400356
×10	4.00356
−4	0.00356
×1000	3.56
−3	0.56
×100	56
−6	50
÷10	5
−5	0

The Place Invader activity can provide an effective indication of the way the place value system works. However, as is the case with the use of base 10 materials, discussion of the processes – why you take away 20 when you want to shoot down the 2 in 328 and what really is happening when you multiply and divide decimal numbers by 10s and 100s and why – is what helps the learning process. If the golden rule – that it is the teacher who teaches, not the materials – is observed, then calculators can provide an invaluable resource for teaching the concept of place value.

Calculators for developing speed and fluency

Peter, a Year 4 class teacher, described the excitement of his children who were involved in a 'Better than a calculator' activity. In this activity Peter paired children and asked one child to do a set of number calculations in the head, whilst the other child worked them out using a calculator. Peter insisted that the child with the calculator used the machine even when she or he could do it in the head. Peter reported that much of the excitement was due to the fact that their mental methods were often faster and that the child using the calculator was slower!

Calculators to encourage estimation and making sense of number operations

Activities which make use of the 'Broken keys' of a calculator are familiar to most of us. These provide excellent opportunities for children to think about the structure of numbers and analyse calculations.

A careful study of the two activities below will show how the calculator is instrumental in encouraging children to perform mental calculations, estimate and think about the structure of numbers. Activity 2, 'Six discrimination', also provides children with opportunities for developing reasoning, communicating, justifying and proving. The response of Asha, a Year 5 child, and her comments, are noteworthy (see page 121).

Activity 1 – Broken Keys

Only the following keys are working on your calculator.

| 3 | 4 | − | × | = |

Can you make the number 100, using just these keys?

Using calculators for exploring properties of numbers

As is emphasised in the *Framework*, calculators can provide an effective way of exploring number properties and number patterns. Previously, I discussed the use of the constant function to generate number patterns. For example, if you want to reinforce doubling and halving, children can use the 'constant function' to generate doubles and halves, in pairs, small groups or with the whole class participating.

Put in number 2, then × followed by 4, you get 8 in the display; each time you press =, the calculator doubles the number giving you 16, 32, 64, 128, and so on. Similarly, the reverse of this should enable to halve the number each time. Try

| 128 | ÷ | 2 | = | = | = |

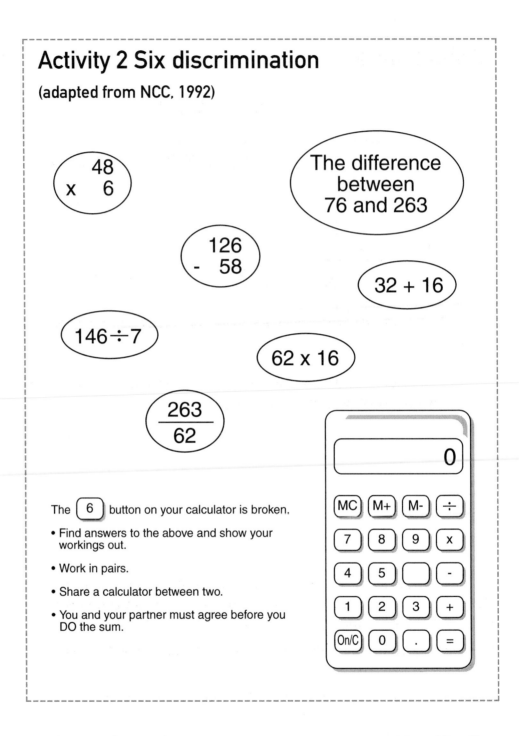

Activity 2 Six discrimination

(adapted from NCC, 1992)

48
x   6

The difference
between
76 and 263

126
-   58

32 + 16

146÷7

62 x 16

263
──
62

The [6] button on your calculator is broken.

- Find answers to the above and show your
  workings out.

- Work in pairs.

- Share a calculator between two.

- You and your partner must agree before you
  DO the sum.

The 'constant function' idea can be used to generate times-tables of 'hard'
numbers such as 19, 27 and so on. The role of the calculator here is for
checking results fast, not cheating.

Calculators can play an important role in learning about properties of
number. Say you want to teach your class how to apply 'divisibility rules'.

Asha's work

```
  4 8        4 8       240
x   6      x   5      + 48
  ___        240      288      = 288
             ___
              4
```

```
126 + 1 5      6 7
- 58 - 5 8    +   1
  ___    6 7    6 8            = 68
```

```
2 6 3  I can't do this because both numbers have 6 in them.
  6 2
```

Usualy I just do the sums, this has helped me think about what the question means.

When children have made their decisions as to the divisibility of numbers, asking them to check them by performing time-consuming algorithms is really moving away from the real objective of that kind of activity.

When a group of Year 6 children were asked to do the number problem:

> If the product of two consecutive numbers is 89700, what are the two numbers?

their teacher, Debbie, allowed the children to use a calculator. She explained her reasons:

> Here I want the children to estimate the answer, think about approximate answers to guide them to the correct solution. I want them to analyse, reason, conjecture and discuss the processes.

Try solving this problem yourself and see if you agree with Debbie's reason for allowing calculators to do the drudgery work whilst her children did the thinking, estimating and mental arithmetic.

When the objective of a lesson is to encourage children to think about complex ideas, the calculator provides a unique resource for this to happen. Try the following idea with a friend or try this with your children.

The great challenge

I divided a 2-digit number by another 2-digit number and the answer given by my calculator was 0.775862. What were the two numbers? Record how you did this.

Group activities such as 'Number Whiz' are designed to develop children's 'feel' for number by considering the size of numbers, analysing and exploring the nature of number operations, estimating approximate answers and developing sound strategies. If you look at the questions carefully, you can see how allowing children to use a calculator to check will release their mental energy so that they can do some real thinking about what is involved in number calculations. If these are done in groups, a great deal of discussion of strategies will be generated.

Number Whiz

You can only use the digits 1, 2, 3, 4, 5, 6 and each digit can be used once only. Using these digits see if you can obtain the following results:

The first one is done for you.

Can you make the answer 390?

Using 254 + 136 = you get 390

The biggest possible answer

□ □ □ + □ □ □ =

The smallest answer

□ □ □ − □ □ □ =

The smallest answer

□ □ □ × □ □ □ =

The biggest answer

□ □ □ × □ □ □ =

Using calculators for problem solving with real numbers

I asked a group of nine year-olds if they thought they had been alive for over a million minutes?

The responses were:

Alex: Don't know, may be.

Me: Can you find out?

Darren: It's too hard. Can't do big numbers like timesing millions.

Me: Do you know how to go about finding out?

Leanne: I suppose so, but I can see big sums coming up. I give up.

Me: What if I do a deal. When you have figured out how to do it and what the calculations are, I will let you use a calculator for the big sums.

The interesting part of this experience was that by the time the group worked out what calculations they needed to do, they no longer wanted to use a calculator! They estimated that they had been alive for more than a million minutes. Here the use of a calculator to do the big sums was used as an incentive to make the group of children embark on a challenging problem activity, which they initially dismissed as not being within their reach because of the 'big' numbers involved!

The use of a calculator, similarly, inspired a group of children to find out how they would work out the 'best buy' items in a children's catalogue which involved working with large numbers, percentages and discounts. According to their teacher, the children would not have attempted a 'real life' type of problem so confidently without the assistance of a calculator. She maintains that children could only use a calculator successfully if they know which operations to use and what the real answers may be like. An example of the need for this kind of awareness of number, or 'number sense', was described by Collette's teacher.

Collette, aged ten, had to work out £67.47 − 57p. When she worked it out on her calculator and got the answer £10.47, she knew straight away that something was wrong. Will all children spot that something is wrong? Collette's group joined in to analyse what may have gone wrong. It took some time to figure out that she had taken away 57p as whole number instead of putting in 57 as a decimal.

Using calculators to play number games

Within the structure of the daily mathematics lesson, the way we use calculator games such as 'Get four-in-a-line' (see Chapter 3) for both whole number and decimal operations will change. It is likely that these games will be played more as team games. *The Decimal Connect 4* game presented below may be simple to you, but try and think about the kind of discussion that could take place if you were to play this as team game.

Decimal Connect 4

This is a game for up to four players or two teams. You need a set of counters, the grid below and a calculator for checking.

Take it in turns to multiply a number in the circle by a number in the rectangle. It helps to estimate the answer first. If your answer is correct, place a counter on the grid. Each time you get a line of 4-vertically, horizontally or diagonally, you win a point. Play until most numbers are covered.

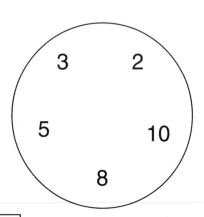

1	0.6	2	3.6	7.5	1.5
31.5	2.5	105	4	53.5	5
52.5	12	1	6	31.5	12
1.5	84	0.6	2	1	12
2.5	105	2.4	6	7.5	84
5	0.6	1.6	3.6	2.4	3

The following comments were made by teachers who tried the *Decimal Connect 4* in their daily mathematics lesson.

◆ 'The calculator acted as a referee; an indispensable, fair and fast referee which enabled everyone to play the game without having to check the answers each time.'

◆ 'Children used their estimation skills to the maximum, encouraged by the urge to win.'

◆ 'They discussed strategies with other members of their team; strategies hitherto not verbalised came up.'

◆ 'When children were allowed to take a copy of the grid home, many children came back having learnt the multiplication facts they needed for playing the game.'

◆ 'The calculator was only a means to promote something very worthwhile. If you don't know your multiplication bonds or how to figure them out, a calculator is of no real help in this situation.'

Using computers to develop numeracy

All the documentation of the National Numeracy Strategy places much emphasis on the centrality of the teacher in developing children's numeracy skills. With this in mind, I will start this section with some responses I have had from teachers when I asked them how they saw computers being used in the daily mathematics lesson and whether they thought how we use computers in mathematics lessons will change when the Numeracy Strategy is in place. The following responses may be worthy of notice:

◆ Most teachers said they did not have a list of available mathematics programmes in their school.

◆ Only 12 out of 78 teachers said they have had any in-service input in the last 6 years, on how to make effective use of computers to teach mathematics.

◆ Several teachers explained they did not have enough hardware to use in the classroom.

◆ Those teachers who used computers in their mathematics teaching felt that the way they use computers will change when the new structured lessons are introduced. The feeling was that computers are more likely to be used for demonstration purposes. It was also felt that many of the programs which are available to schools may involve children only in repeating skills they already have; time which they cannot afford to waste. If the school had a network, it was felt, then children could have a problem solving lesson using *Logo*, databases or spreadsheets, with the teacher explaining principles to all children at the same time and then offer individual support to those children who need it.

◆ There are so few programs available for 'early years' mathematics, it would be a waste of time using computers for the sake of using them.

A close look at the responses given above highlights the fact that, in spite of the general endorsement of the use of computers, the reality is that teachers will need considerable support, not only in terms of more hardware and software, but on ways in which they can make effective use of computers. We are reassured in the Final Report of the National Numeracy Taskforce (DfEE, 1999) that with the government's commitment to ICT training from 1999, the role of ICT in the teaching of mathematics will be an important aspect of that training.

Does ICT support mathematics teaching and learning? Research suggests (Askew and William, 1995) that computers have a substantial positive impact on pupils' achievement in mathematics.

In 1995 I attempted (Koshy and Dodds, 1995) to list types of computer software and how they may be used to enhance mathematics learning. The list included:

◆ **Programing languages** such as Logo which can be used to create both geometrical and number patterns. Logo is also a very powerful problem-solving tool.

◆ **Structured programs** which are designed to help children to develop concepts and acquire mathematical facts. These programs often offer opportunities for practising skills and reinforcement. These programs can also offer a good alternative to working through text books because many of them are presented in motivating contexts and provide instant feedback to children. As we all know, children are often happier to accept mistakes being pointed out by a computer than by the teacher. Some structured programs are in the form of investigations which encourage children to develop processes for problem solving. These programs are particularly useful because the computer can generate more drawings and models than the human hand can and it can also help children to make predictions and test hypotheses.

◆ **Databases and spreadsheets**, which are content-free, can be used for collecting, sorting, representing and interpreting data. These involve both learning number facts and using number in problem solving.

In the following section I will provide some examples of how teachers use computer programs with children. The examples are drawn from the work of a range of age groups and types of software. Only aspects which are related to developing numeracy skills are explored. I am assuming that either teachers are familiar with the packages mentioned or will consult manuals and handbooks for any necessary technical information.

The purpose of providing these activities is twofold: first, they give you information on the software available and the nature of the activities you can plan; the second is to enable you to consider the best ways of using the software for developing numerical skills. While you read this section it may be worthwhile for you to consider two questions about each activity.

◆ What aspect of numeracy can children learn from this activity?

◆ What is the best way to introduce and develop this activity?

Using roamers and floor turtles

Before introducing children to floor turtles, it is a good idea to ask pairs of children to pretend they are floor turtles and give instructions to each other, perhaps blind-folded, to get to a destination to collect a 'mystery prize'. Child A gives instructions to Child B:

Move forward 10 steps, turn right by half turn, move 5 more steps and so on. Child B moves according to the instructions.

You may then make it more challenging by creating some obstacles on the way which make it necessary to 'estimate' more effectively and to be more accurate with instructions.

In an infant classroom, I was impressed by the quality of instructions given to the dressed up floor turtle to deliver letters to a row of houses (on a map) numbered 1 to 12. The class teacher analysed the skills required to do this activity as:

- knowing number names and vocabulary relating to space;

- knowing directions;

- knowing the correspondence between a number name and what it stands for – the cardinal aspect of number;

- estimating;

- verbalising and communicating instructions and strategies;

- knowing the order in which numbers appear on a number line – the ordinal spect.

Floor turtles and roamers can be used with maps or nursery rhymes and fairy tales, so that children can programme the turtles to visit places on the maps.

Floor turtles to screen turtles

The *Logo* program on the screen presents you with a arrow head which acts as the turtle. It understands the concept of direction and units of distance in number.

Try putting an acetate maze on the computer screen and ask a group of children to give instructions to get to a destination. You can experience for yourself the enhanced level of motivation and spatial and number talk amongst the group.

The following activities are worthwhile for programming turtles on the screen:

◆ Ask children to draw polygons and list what they have learnt by doing so.

◆ Can you draw this rocket?

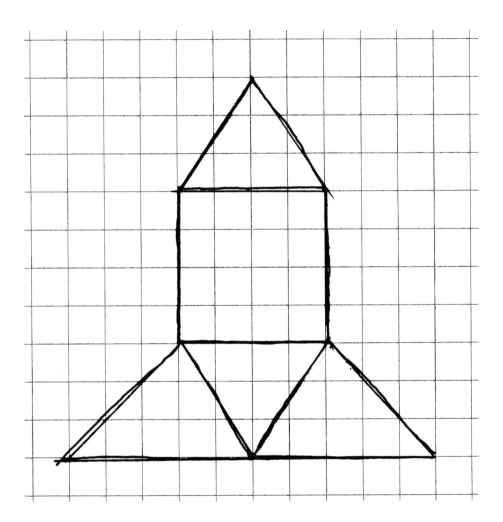

◆ A group of children could create a shape frieze, collectively, which enables mixed ability groups to work together on a problem-solving project.

We often underestimate children's capability to programme in *Logo*. HMI (1985) shows the following as an example of a pattern which could be created by infant age groups.

Try this with the children.

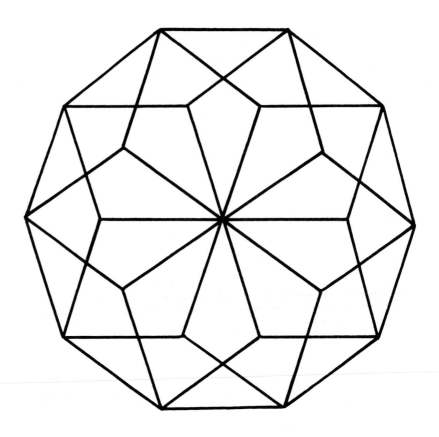

Number programs

Recently I worked with a group of primary teachers at the SMILE centre (see Resources) evaluating some of their software for teaching numeracy.

Programs such as 'Guess' (SMILE) are designed to let children think about the concept of a number line and the relative sizes of numbers. In this activity, children are asked to guess the computer's number, with feedback given on the size of the number. This kind of activity can be used either for demonstration purposes at the start of a lesson or as part of the main lesson for a selected groups of children who may need to practise with these concepts.

Another program called 'number line', from (SMILE), provides challenging opportunities for children to use blank number lines at different levels. I have watched groups of teachers and children using this program and was impressed by the amount of discussion and use of mathematical vocabulary generated by the activity. Again, this program is ideal for demonstration purposes because of its visual impact, as well as its facility of offering graded levels of difficulty. These programs are also very useful for assessment purposes, as the motivation aspect of the activity makes children talk more freely and try their best.

Demonstration programs

Whilst the programs discussed above model number lines and deal with number sizes, programs such as 'Angles' and 'Take half' (SMILE) focus on particular concepts. These can also be used for whole class demonstration purposes. The effectiveness of these, of course, will depend on the nature and quality of the questions asked by the teacher. After introducing children to such activities they can be asked to explore the ideas further and perhaps put up an interactive display of the ideas addressed in the programs.

Using databases

Databases are like card file systems which can store a great deal of information. This information can be sorted and searched within seconds. As this often involves collecting, sorting and representing numerical data, children's numerical skills are developed as a result.

You can use a database for a simple investigation of the children's favourite sweets. Alison, a Year 1 teacher, did this with the whole class. With a flip chart to record the data, she asked her children what they thought the class's favourite sweet was. The teacher wrote down all the names of sweets suggested. The data were then put into a database and graphs drawn.

An analysis of this activity was convincing evidence of its usefulness. There was counting, comparison of the size of numbers and ordering numbers, all in a problem-solving situation. Many of the problem-solving strategies recommended in the *Framework* were in evidence.

Creating databases of body measurements is another motivating activity. This type of investigation can range from simple explorations of body heights to establishing relationships between various parts of the body. Questions such as:

> *The rumour is that three times the length of your headband is the same as your height. Is this true?*

> *Are we all squares? Is our height the same as our handspan?*

> *Do boys have bigger heads?*

Besides learning how to handle data, these investigations also provide opportunities for children to communicate with mathematics and develop their problem-solving skills.

Using spreadsheets

We can describe a spreadsheet as an electronic sheet which is set out with a number of boxes called 'cells' and grids of 'rows' and 'columns'. It can store and calculate numbers with accuracy and speed. Those who want to find out more about the principles of how to use spreadsheets with children should find it useful to read the section on Spreadsheets in Janet Ainley's (1997) book *Enriching Primary Mathematics with IT*. Her examples of using spreadsheets show how these can be useful for developing children's numerical skills.

	A	B	C	D	E	F	G	H
1								
2	1	3	5	7	9	11	13	15

Changing this number will create different patterns

The simple spreadsheet idea shown here demonstrates how number patterns are generated by typing 1 into A2, putting formula A2 + 2 into cell B2 and then filling along row B. This process can be used to generate number patterns of increasing complexity; odd numbers, multiples of 4, counting back in jumps of 8, times tables of 19 or 28! Or you can generate square numbers or cube numbers. The process of finding the right formula to make these patterns will generate much talk about the properties of number.

Children are also fascinated by the fact that you can create and change the type of graph very easily. Consider conducting an investigation into Smarties in different tubes. Ask children to pose some questions they would like to explore, such as:

◆ How many smarties are there in a tube?

◆ Do they all have the same number of smarties?

◆ Do all the tubes have the same colour distribution?

Ask children to work in groups to investigate the questions and put up a display.

Other uses of ICT to support the teaching of mathematics

Websites

As the government initiative for developing ICT in schools progresses, there will be many more opportunities for ICT to support the teaching and learning of mathematics. At present there are many websites available for teachers to consult, for resources, for research findings, for mathematics clubs and so on.

Displays and publications

Word processing packages and desk-top packages offer many opportunities for children to be involved in creating class mathematical displays, making mathematics puzzles and games. Production of an in-house numeracy journal is another possibility.

Summary

In this chapter I considered different ways in which ICT can support the teaching of numeracy, with a special focus on the role of calculators and computers. Different views on the usefulness of calculators were considered and some practical ways of using calculators for developing children's numerical competence were explored. The types of computer software available and their potential for learning mathematics were considered. Although the full potential of computers is not utilised for mathematics teaching, with the forthcoming expansion of ICT facilities in schools, new opportunities will arise.

Chapter 6

Differentiation for the ability spectrum

Planning and teaching activities which match children's abilities have always been the most challenging of tasks for a teacher. During the past decade, especially since the Education Reform Act (1988) and the National Curriculum came into existence, the word 'differentiation' has been used to describe the process of meeting the curriculum needs of children of different abilities and potential. School inspection reports, in recent years, have highlighted the need for more effective differentiation.

Differentiation

What is differentiation? Although most of us know what it entails, it is not so easy to define. Perhaps we don't need to define it. Kershner and Miles (1996) quote a headteacher, who like many of us, had difficulties with a definition:

> We seem to be looking for a global definition for differentiation. I don't think we can have one. I think it's a term that, I suppose like bar of soap really, you try to grasp it and suddenly it shoots out of your hand. (p. 17)

For the purpose of this book, I will use the term differentiation to mean ways in which we make adaptations to the offered curriculum. With that description in mind, I will suggest some practical ways of how we may achieve it. First, what is the view of the National Numeracy Strategy about differentiation? The Numeracy Task Force (DfEE, 1998) has this to say under the heading 'Differentiation' with the subheading 'Dealing with a range of attainment':

> It is clear from inspection and other evidence that the range of attainment in mathematics in the classrooms, particularly at the upper end of Key Stage 2, is currently too wide. The aim of our recommended strategy is to allow all the children in a class to progress steadily, so that all of them reach a satisfactory standard and the range of attainment is much narrower. We are concerned that children should not continue to work at many different levels, with the teacher placing them in a wide range of differentiated groups. (p. 54)

Concerns

One of the first questions to consider is: what do practising teachers think? From the discussions I have had with teachers, it is evident that they feel that one of the major challenges in the implementation of the National Numeracy Strategy is differentiation. Dealing with the spectrum of abilities within the classroom, in the context of the daily mathematics lesson, needs careful consideration. Samples of teachers' comments, quoted below, may help us to understand the problem before considering practical strategies for addressing the concerns.

> In our school we have a very mixed intake. In each class, we have quite a large number of children who need special attention. We are not talking about one or two here. There are at least eight children in my Year 5 class who cannot cope with numbers up to 100, whilst the others are working with large numbers and decimals. There is no way I can teach them all together every day, for 20 minutes a day – for the introduction and plenary. (Alison)

> The classroom reality is that I have about half a dozen children who would put their hands up for everything and another six or seven children who will not want to contribute anything to save embarrassment because they may get the answers wrong, nor will they have anything to contribute during plenaries. Asking easier questions is one way of doing it; but many of them feel I am patronising them with simple questions. (Anna)

> The problem with mathematics is that children need some pre-requisite skills in order to learn newer ideas. For example, it is difficult to teach addition of 2-digit numbers with carrying to the whole group when I know that some of them are struggling with counting up to 100. They have to be taught separately, so that they don't lose the small amount of self-esteem they have. (Stuart)

> In my Year 4 class I have about three children who are very bright, they have such a passion for mathematics and one of them is really exceptional – Andrew – who is being prepared for GCSE by his parents. I cannot imagine them, especially Andrew, sitting through whole-class lessons every day. (Jackie)

An analysis of teachers' comments, including the ones quoted above, helped me to summarise some of their concerns. They are:

◆ difficulties with teaching a mixed-ability group in a given time;

◆ concerns about meeting the needs of very able children who enjoy spending time figuring things out and who have the stamina to keep going with investigations;

◆ children who already know what is going to be taught may switch off, or be frustrated;

◆ children who need special attention and support because they are slower learners or have problems understanding instructions;

◆ pressure from parents of very able children and those who are being coached for grammar school or independent school entry.

A close look at the list of concerns will show that many of them are not particularly related of the implementation of the National Numeracy Strategy. The challenge of meeting the needs of children with learning difficulties and those of very able mathematicians have always been with us. Headteachers have often articulated to me their dilemma over the conflicting objectives of having to achieve more Level 4s in the Standard Assessment Tasks and giving special time and attention to their able pupils. The main concerns, particularly associated with the National Numeracy Strategy, were time restrictions and the recommendation to teach the whole class for a large part of the time.

Strategies for effective differentiation

We looked at what differentiation means and the concerns raised by teachers about the practical difficulties of teaching children of different abilities, aptitudes and learning speeds together in a whole class situation. The next step is to think about some useful strategies which can address the concerns. Practising teachers have found the following ideas useful.

Organisation

One of the ways in which schools have been able to cater for the mixed abilities in a class is to set the children for mathematics lessons. This reduces the range of abilities and enables the teacher to be involved in whole class teaching for most of the daily mathematics lesson. The questions and explanations can be targeted at roughly the same level. Children are able to work with peers of similar ability for group tasks. Lower achievers feel more secure and less anxious when they are not constantly aware that they are behind their peers. For more able children, this type of organisation provides opportunities to undertake challenging tasks with others. The teacher may not feel the need to bring the lesson to a final conclusion every day. For example, she could ask children to report to the group about two ideas they are now dealing with or are puzzled about, making it possible to carry on with an extended investigation or make it part of homework.

In some ways, setting is not very different to what we were used to in the past. In many classrooms children are grouped according to ability and children do know which ability group they belong to. I know this because I am told by children, during my visits to see teacher training students, that they belong to the top group, or middle group and sometimes they even describe themselves as the 'dunce group'. A school deciding to set children for mathematics needs to carefully consider whether setting by ability within the classroom is better or worse for the children involved and for their self-esteem.

A few further points about setting. In many schools, the most experienced teacher is given the top mathematics group; this practice needs consideration too. If the aim of setting or grouping by ability is to *raise* achievement and *narrow the gap* between the groups, as required by the National Numeracy Strategy, who teaches the lower sets becomes a real issue. The need for flexibility of movement between groups is also important for the children. Mistakes may be made at the time of the initial assessment of children; even tiredness, nervousness or boredom with tests and having to find convergent solutions to questions can affect test results. The other point to remember is the way the criteria for setting is communicated to the parents. In one school parents were told at a parents meeting that what was taught in all three sets was based on exactly the same syllabus, but the teaching was at different speeds and levels of depth of enquiry. This perhaps simple explanation satisfied the parents. In that particular school, interim tests showed that the middle group was obtaining higher scores than the top set; this was interesting too. The issue of setting is a complex one, but many teachers believe that this is one of the inevitable consequences of tests and league tables.

If you decide not to set children, you may need to think of ways of grouping children according to their experience and abilities during the daily mathematics lesson. For example, within a whole class introduction, you may ask children to work in pairs or in small groups for a few minutes before they answer questions. The main teaching activity provides another opportunity for a group of similar ability to work together, discuss tasks and prepare for the plenary session. A child of exceptional ability may be able to work individually or work with an adult who can support him or her with mathematics at a higher level than that being taught to the rest of the class.

Here is another point about teaching mathematics to the top set. The content of what is being taught to brighter children needs to be considered. If these children are given more of the type of work they have already mastered or photocopies of closed problem-solving activities, the whole purpose of setting is defeated. Being bright becomes a punishable offence! Some kind of curriculum compacting which involves stream-lining repetitive work may be necessary. These children are likely to be capable of thinking about ideas in more depth and being involved in enquiries which demand a greater degree of knowledge, as well as understanding of concepts.

Adjustments also have to be made, both in the content and teaching style, for the children in the lower set. The content may have to be specially designed with smaller steps of progression. These steps may be more achievable. As the achievement of objectives may take longer, the nature of praise and acknowledgement given to the children may need to be considered.

Effective questioning

Planning the type of questions you ask is a key issue in differentiated provision. For the introductory part of the lesson, when the whole class is working together, you need to plan in advance what questions to ask and who is to be asked the questions. For example, if you want to initiate a doubling activity with the whole class – choose a number less than 5, double it and keep doubling it – you may target the simpler numbers at children who you know can only cope with smaller numbers. This may also be the case when the activity is based on 'guess my number'. If the number chosen needs very sophisticated questioning, you may target the more able ones first. In one classroom I saw a function machine activity, when children had to guess what the output numbers would be after the machine had 'operated' on the input number. Here the teacher selected questions of graded difficulty for different children.

You also need to consider the type of questions you ask children, in their differentiated groups, during the main activity. You may include questions which involve a degree of analysis for the brighter group. An example of this was seen in a Year 5 class working on number operations. The teacher felt that the children needed to think about what they were actually doing when 'carrying' and 'exchanging' tens and hundreds. So, one of the questions she included was:

> Pretend you are in Spiderland. Our number system is base 10 because we have ten fingers. Instead of having base ten, spiders work in base 8 as they have eight legs. Can you work out what a page of Spiders' sums would be like? Try and work out what the times tables would look like in Spiderland.

Another way to extend children's thinking is by asking the question: what if . . . what if not, and so on leading children to conjecture, prove and generalise.

During the plenary session, differentiated questions could be asked according to your assessment of what individual children may have learnt in a session. Whilst discussing what the children have learnt about fractions, you may ask a range of questions which include: show me, on the board, pictures of two fraction ideas you have learnt. Can you mime a fraction for the rest of the class or can you think about any advantages in being a fraction rather than a whole number?

The choice of activities

For providing differentiation you need to plan activities which result in a range of outcomes. Most teachers are familiar with two types of

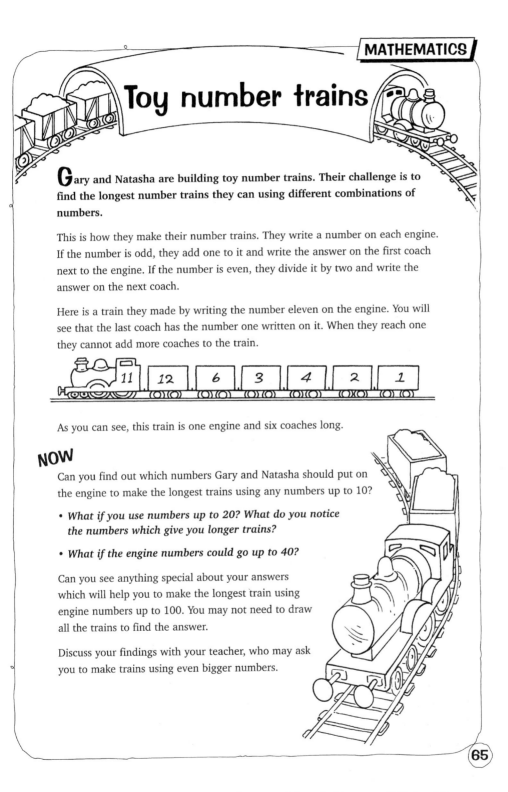

MATHEMATICS

Toy number trains

Gary and Natasha are building toy number trains. Their challenge is to find the longest number trains they can using different combinations of numbers.

This is how they make their number trains. They write a number on each engine. If the number is odd, they add one to it and write the answer on the first coach next to the engine. If the number is even, they divide it by two and write the answer on the next coach.

Here is a train they made by writing the number eleven on the engine. You will see that the last coach has the number one written on it. When they reach one they cannot add more coaches to the train.

| 11 | 12 | 6 | 3 | 4 | 2 | 1 |

As you can see, this train is one engine and six coaches long.

NOW

Can you find out which numbers Gary and Natasha should put on the engine to make the longest trains using any numbers up to 10?

- *What if you use numbers up to 20? What do you notice the numbers which give you longer trains?*

- *What if the engine numbers could go up to 40?*

Can you see anything special about your answers which will help you to make the longest train using engine numbers up to 100. You may not need to draw all the trains to find the answer.

Discuss your findings with your teacher, who may ask you to make trains using even bigger numbers.

65

Figure 6.1 Toy Number Trains from *Bright Challenge* published by Stanley Thornes

differentiation – differentiation by task and differentiation by outcome. During the main part of the mathematics lesson you may decide to give your children a set of word problems which produce only one solution per problem. The outcome is fixed, but within that structure you could design the problems in such a way that some of them involve only one step whilst others may involve multiple steps. It may be that some problems will involve working with complex data whilst others involve simpler numbers.

Open-ended problems help to differentiate by outcome. I will illustrate this with the example of a class of eight year-olds working on the investigation 'Toy number trains' (see page 139).

Most of the children in the class halved the numbers, added one on and so on and were very satisfied with the outcome when they worked out that number 9 gave them the longest train. Another group worked out, by drawing trains, that number 17 gave them the longest train between 1 and 20. Some others abandoned drawing trains and recorded just the numbers on a 'tree' and after a while noticed that the numbers 9, 17, 33, 65 and so on gave longer trains; only with the teacher's help did they see that these numbers were the result of powers of 2 + 1.

Similarly, the question: *How many diagonals can you draw for a 5-sided polygon, then an eight sided one? 12-sided?* was investigated by a Year 6 group of children. After the lesson, all the children knew what a polygon and a diagonal was. Most children could draw and work out that a five-sided polygon has 5 diagonals. A few children entered the number of diagonals for 6- and 7-sided polygons, by drawing the shapes and looking at the pattern by which the number of diagonals grew. With some encouragement and prompts from the teacher, two children spotted a rule that the number of diagonals could be obtained by $\frac{1}{2}$ n (n-3). The successful differentiation achieved with both the train activity and the diagonal activity was due to the choice of activity with a range of possible outcomes.

Using appropriate resources

To some extent, resources can support differentiation. A range of visual aids, big books and games which are designed to provide reinforcement may help children who have special learning difficulties. They may need to use practical apparatus for longer periods than the rest of the class. Information and Communications Technology also has much to offer children at both ends of the spectrum. Able mathematicians can access problem-solving materials, investigations and both national and international competitions through the internet; NRICH (see *Resources*), is one such example. It is a good idea to have mathematics magazines and puzzles of different levels of challenge in the classroom.

The Framework suggests that children can also be given additional support or extension activities during the week, in each term when no topic is allocated on the planning grid. This may take the form of reinforcement activities or an extended piece of investigation. It may be used for constructing or working out a numeracy trail. Different children can be given roles and responsibilities according to their capabilities, so that every child feels valued and is given a chance to use his or her talents.

Homework

Most schools now give homework to children. This is an excellent opportunity for some targeted provision for different groups of children. For example, very able children may be given an extended piece of work which they can carry out over two or three days. They are more likely to research independently through books or by asking other people around them. Many of our teachers encourage children to keep mathematics diaries in which they write notes about their mathematics investigations. One school encourages children to construct their own glossaries – one or two mathematical words at a time. One such example is given below.

Decimal Numbers

Decimal numbers are parts of whole numbers. The decimal point seperates whole numbers from decimal numbers. The number that comes after a decimal point is a fraction of a number. For example 6·4, this number has six whole numbers and four parts of a number.

Another example is...

$$25·05.$$

twenty five whole numbers.

decimal point.

not a whole number. $\left(\text{It is } \frac{5}{100}\right)$

Asha.

Children who need extra practice with number bonds or number facts can also be given tasks to be done at home. It is pertinent to add here that it is a myth that bright children are always numerate. I have worked with groups of very able children whose numerical skills were weak and prevented them from carrying out advanced work which was otherwise within their capability.

Differentiation is a challenge, but it can be achieved through careful assessment of children's abilities, aptitudes, experiences and interests.

Using outside support

If external support is available, this should be fully utilised for meeting the curriculum needs of children. In the daily mathematics lessons the presence of a volunteer – parent, friend of the school, a teacher from the local secondary school – willing to give a few hours can be very valuable. Perhaps an old pupil could provide some additional support for children. Many schools have mathematics clubs and extension programmes which are supported with external help. Voluntary external agencies are also worth approaching.

Summary

In this chapter aspects of differentiation were explored. Teachers' concerns about providing a differentiated curriculum within the structure of the daily mathematics lesson were considered. Some strategies for effective differentiation were discussed.

Bibliography

Ainley, J. (1996) *Enriching Primary Mathematics with IT*. London: Hodder & Stoughton.

Askew, M. (1997a) *Teaching Primary Mathematics: A guide for newly qualified and student teachers*. London: Hodder & Stoughton.

Askew et al (1997) *Raising Attainment in Primary Numeracy: Report of a project funded by Nuffield Foundation*. London: Kings College.

Askew, M., Brown, M., Rhodes, V., William, D. and Johnson, D. (1997b) *Effective Teachers of Numeracy: A report of a study carried out for the Teacher Training Agency*. London: Kings College, University of London.

Askew, M. and William, D. (1995) *Recent Research in Mathematics Education*. London: HMSO.

Assessment of Performance Unit (1982) *Mathematical Development: Primary Survey No. 3.* London: HMSO.

Assessment of Performance Unit (1985) *Mathematical Development: A Review in Monitoring in Mathematics*. London: HMSO.

Association for Teachers of Mathematics (1991) *Exploring Mathematics with Younger Children*. Derby: ATM.

Brown, M. (1981) 'Place value and decimals' in Hart, K. (ed) *Children's Understanding of Mathematics*. London: John Murray.

Burghes, D. (1999) 'Mathematics Enhancement Programme: Demonstration Project' in *Mathematics in Schools*, May 1999.

Burghes, D. and Merttens, R. (1997) *A Blueprint for Numeracy*. Handout from conference in London.

Callahan, J. (1976) Speech delivered at Ruskin College, Oxford.

Casey, R. and Koshy, V. (1995) *Bright Challenge Key Stage 2*. Glos: Stanley Thornes.

Cockcroft, W.H. (1982) *Mathematics Counts. Report of the Committee of Inquiry into the Teaching of Mathematics in Schools*. London: HMSO.

DES (1987) *National Curriculum Task Group for Assessment and Testing*. London: HMSO.

DES (1991) *Mathematics in the National Curriculum*. London: HMSO.

DfEE (1998) *The Implementation of the National Numeracy Strategy; The final report of the Numeracy Task Force*. London: Department for Education and Employment.

DfEE (1999) *The Framework for Teaching Mathematics*. London Department for Education and Employment.

DfEE (1995) *Mathematics in the National Curriculum*. London: HMSO.

DfEE (1999) *Three-day course. Notes for course tutors*. London: DfEE.

Duffin, J. (1997) 'The role of calculators' in Thompson, I. (ed) *Teaching and Learning Early Number*. Milton Keynes: Open University Press.

Fielker, D. (1997) *Extending Mathematical Ability Through Whole Class Teaching* London: Hodder & Stoughton.

Hart, K. et al (1989) *Children's Mathematical Frameworks 8–13: A study of Classroom Teaching*. Windsor: NFER–Nelson.

HMI (1978) *Primary Education in England*. London: HMSO.

HMI (1979) *Aspects of Secondary Education in England*. London: HMSO.

HMI (1985) *Mathematics 5–16: Curriculum Matters 3*. London: HMSO.

Hughes, M. (1986) *Children and Number: Difficulties in Learning Mathematics* Oxford: Basil Blackwell.

Kershner, R. and Miles, S. (1996) 'Thinking and talking about differentiation' in Bearne, E. (ed) *Differentiation and Diversity*. London: Routledge.

Koshy, V. (1988) *Place Value: An investigation of Children's Strategies and Errors and an Evaluation of a Teaching Programme*. Unpublished M.Phil. Dissertation. Kings College, London.

Koshy, V. and Dodds, P. (1995) *Making IT Work for You*. Glos: Stanley Thornes.

Koshy, V. (1998) *Mental Maths Teachers' Book 9–11*. London: Collins.

Mitchell, C. and Koshy, V. (1995) *Effective Teacher Assessment: Looking at Children's Learning*. London: Hodder & Stoughton.

National Curriculum Council (1992) *Using and Applying Mathematics Book B*. York: NCC.

Ofsted (1993) *The Teaching and Learning of Number in Primary Schools*. London: HMSO.

Ofsted (1994) *Mathematics and Science in Schools*. London: HMSO.

Ofsted (1998) *The National Numeracy Project: An HMI Evaluation*. London: Office for Standards in Education.

Ofsted (1998) *Teachers Count* – Video tape.

Qualifications and Curriculum and Authority (2000) *Mathematics National Curriculum*. London: QCA.

Pinel, A. (1988) *Loop Cards*. Address: 39, Tennyson Rd, Bognor Regis, West Sussex.

SCAA (1997) *The Teaching and Assessment of Number at Key Stages 1–3*. Discussion Paper No. 10 March 1997.

Straker, A. (1993) *Talking Points in Mathematics*. Cambridge: Cambridge University Press.

Thompson, I. (1999) 'Prop or tool' in *Times Education Supplement*, March 12, 1999.

Resources

▬ ▬

Useful equipment

Number lines 0–10; 0–20, 0–100, marked in tens, hundreds, fraction lines, decimal lines and blank strips

Digit cards 0–9, several sets

Arrow cards

Calculators

Base ten blocks

Number cards 1–100

Dice

Spinners

Recommended books for practical ideas

Beam catalogue provides an extensive list of very good resources; only a few are listed here.

Address
Beam Education
Maze workshops
72a Southgate Road
London N1 3JT

Exploring Fractions
Exploring Decimals
Exploring Place Value
Number at Key Stage 1
Number at Key Stage 2
Starting from your head: Mental number
Starting from number lines

Collins Publishers provide a range of effective materials. Their mental maths series provides practical ideas.

Address
Collins Educational
77–85 Fulham Palace Road
London W6. 8BJ

Collins Mental Maths Teacher's Guide Ages 5–7

Collins Mental Maths Teacher's Guide Ages 7–9

Collins Mental Maths Teacher's Guide Ages 9–11

The *Association of Teachers of Mathematics* has a catalogue of publications; their problem-solving and investigation materials are particularly good.

Address
ATM
7 Shaftesbury Street
Derby DE23 8YB

Exploring Mathematics with Younger Children

Primary Points of Departure

Computer resources

Mindstorms by Seymour Papert is a very useful book to read. Papert argues powerfully how problem-solving using Logo helps children's mathematics learning.

British Educational Communications and Technology Agency (BECTA — used to be known as NCET) — http://www.ncet.org.uk — provides a very useful list of support systems for using ICT.

Address
Millburn Hill Road
Science Park
Coventry CV4 7JJ

SMILE provides a very good range of software to support numeracy.

Address
Isaac Newton Centre
108a Lancaster Road
London W11 1QS

Useful website

NRICH: http://nrich.maths.org.uk/ This is an online maths club which should be of particular help for extensions activities.

Index